PADEREWSKI: PIANIST AND PATRIOT

Mr. Paderewski and three-year-old Binky Stewart in a scene from
Moonlight Sonata

PADEREWSKI

Pianist and Patriot

by

ANTONI GRONOWICZ

Rendered in English by Jessie McEwen

DRAWINGS BY GEORGE AVISON

1943

THOMAS NELSON AND SONS

Edinburgh　　　New York　　　Toronto

BY THE SAME AUTHOR

BOLEK

COPYRIGHT, 1943

by ANTONI GRONOWICZ

All rights reserved

Contents

Contents

Illustrations

One

Ignacy and His Friend Siwek

The day was a golden one at the end of July and the year was 1870. The humming of the bees, homeward bound to their white-capped hives, and well-laden with nectar, made a steady, ceaseless drone in the clear air. The brilliant sun beat down relentlessly on the flowers, on the ripened grain in the harvest fields, and on the harvesters, stooped over their tasks of cutting and sheaving. At last the flowers bent their heads as if to hide their faces from the sun's heat, and soon the harvesters sought respite from its heat and glare under the shade of the wide-branching trees that stood in clumps along the border of the fields.

A passerby on the dusty road might have paused to wonder

at this unusual occurrence. Cloudless, sunny skies, ripened grain, and the harvesters lying under the trees — a most remarkable sight! And especially so, as the fields were part of the estate of Count Tyszkiewicz, whose estate manager was known throughout the district of Sudylkow for his strict discipline. Mr. Jan Paderewski, for that was the manager's name, seldom showed any consideration for harvesters who could not work on throughout the day, despite the sun's brightness and heat. However, one would not have had to look far, on this day, for an explanation of Mr. Paderewski's generosity. It was yonder, near the white house that was his home.

The house was no different than usual. It stood on a little hill above a dirty, stagnant pond, and its green lawns sloped away to a Jewish cemetery. The remarkable thing, and therein was the explanation of Mr. Paderewski's surprising deviation from his usual stern discipline, was the great throng of children playing in the garden in front of the house. There were many children of many ages and many nationalities: some Jewish, some Russian, some Ukrainian, some Polish. And all were gay and noisy. A boy of ten stood in the midst of this boisterous gathering, receiving greetings and giving welcome to his friends. This boy was Ignacy Paderewski, only son of the estate administrator, and this sunny July day was his name day— Saint Ignacy Day—and his father had invited his friends and his son's friends to a celebration. Soon the harvesters would leave the shade of the trees and, instead of returning with their scythes and rakes and forks to the fields, they would join their fellow-villagers at the feast.

"It is a wonderful party, Antonina," Ignacy exclaimed to

his sister. "Never before in my life have I had such a party."

His sister laughed and said, "You are young yet, Ignacy, not quite ten. In the future you will likely have many parties."

Antonina spoke in a very grown-up manner, as if she had behind her the experiences of many more years than her brother. As a matter of fact, she was just two years older than Ignacy.

"Come, let us go to the meadow," Ignacy called out now to his young guests. "We can play games there, and you will see me feed cookies to Siwek."

In an instant, he was off, followed by an approving group of barefooted boys and girls. He went so swiftly that Antonina had to run after him in order to call him back.

"You must not go now, Ignacy," she protested.

But Ignacy, unheeding, ran on, and Antonina followed, protesting all the time. Finally the boy stopped and asked with more than a shade of impatience in his voice, "Why must we not go to the meadow?"

"You know very well why not," Antonina said severely. "You know that Count Chodkiewicz and Baron Horoch are coming to hear you play the piano. They will arrive at any moment. Indeed, they may have come already."

"Well, what of it?" Ignacy was very lofty. "When one goes to a concert one waits for the music. That is the usual thing."

"How do you know it is, Ignacy?" one boy asked. "Have you been to many concerts?"

"No," Ignacy answered promptly, "but I know, for Piotr Sowinski has described many concerts to me, and has told me how he and all the audience have waited and waited for the musicians to appear. Besides, Mr. Runowski has said the same thing. The people must wait for the musician."

Piotr Sowinski was Ignacy Paderewski's music teacher. Mr. Runowski was an old violinist who was much interested in the boy, because of the promise he gave of being a gifted musician.

"Count Chodkiewicz and Baron Horoch may not wait for you," Antonina warned. "People wait for famous musicians, not for little boys."

It was easy to see that Antonina was angry with her brother. Her cheeks were flushed and she put her hand on his arm as if to turn him back to the house.

But Ignacy would not be deterred from his course. He escaped Antonina's detaining hand and said, "Come on, let's go to the meadow," and with a laugh added, "I'll be a famous musician some day. You'll see."

There was nothing for Antonina to do but follow her brother. She walked slowly, anger and fear and perplexity mingling in her expression. Her friend Mila walked with her; the others rushed on in a cloud of dust behind Ignacy.

"They'll wait," Mila tried to reassure Antonina. "After all, the count and the baron know this is Ignacy's name day. They'll know that Siwek should have a share in the celebration."

Siwek was Ignacy's horse and they were faithful friends.

"Our mother will be angry with us," Antonina said. "It isn't that she minds Ignacy feeding Siwek cookies. It is that he will keep those two men waiting to hear him play the piano. She will be very angry."

"Your mother!" Mila exclaimed impatiently. "Why do you

Ignacy and his sister, Antonina

call her your mother? Isn't your mother dead? Mrs. Paderewski is just your stepmother." Mila liked relationships to be
well defined.

"To be sure, but that does not matter," Antonina answered,
"for she is good to us, and Ignacy knows as well as I do that our
father wants us to obey her."

Antonina and Mila had now arrived in the great meadow.
If the sister had not been so disturbed by her brother's conduct, she might have noticed the rich fragrance of the field.
The flowers and the new-cut grass smelled like incense in a
village church.

The boys and girls were clustered around Ignacy and his
silvery gray horse, and Ignacy was busy taking cookies from
his pockets and giving them to Siwek. There was no doubt
about it—Siwek found cookies delicious eating.

From the first day that Ignacy Paderewski had come to
Sudylkow, he and the gray horse, Siwek, had been fast friends.
They had gone together, sometimes with Ignacy walking and
sometimes riding on Siwek's back, over the meadows and
through the forests of the neighboring countryside. Siwek, of
his own accord, had devised an easy way for the boy to mount:
he bent his head low, and let Ignacy climb over it and on to
his back. On occasions, when they roamed through the deep
woods, they had been attacked by wild dogs, but Siwek was
always quick to protect his young master. Even with Ignacy
mounted, he could kick the dogs so thoroughly that the animals would go off whimpering. Once at least, according to
what the boy had told Antonina, Siwek had bitten a bold dog
that had fended off his kicks.

It was no more than natural, since they were such loyal friends, that on this important day Ignacy's first thought should be for Siwek, his protector as well as his friend. Antonina had meant to take her brother by the hand and drag him back to the house, but now, like their guests, she stood watching the two of them. Ignacy certainly loved Siwek, and as she watched Siwek nuzzle his pink nose into the boy's hand, she knew that Siwek loved Ignacy quite as much.

"You say that you and Siwek have been friends from your first day in Sudylkow," Ivan, the son of the count's hunchbacked water-carrier, remarked. "To me that seems very strange. I always thought a friendship had to grow between a boy and a dumb animal."

"Oh, no, not at all," Ignacy answered. "When we lived in Kurylowka in Podole we had a horse that loved me just as much as Siwek does now."

"That horse was shot by the czarist police," Antonina said.

"Tell us about it," the children cried out instantly. "Did you see it happen?"

One or two children, older than the others, begged to be told something about Kurylowka, too. To them, unaccustomed to travel, Kurylowka in Podole seemed like a strange and distant land. That was one reason why they found the Paderewski children so interesting: they had not lived all their lives on the estate of Count Tyszkiewicz.

"You tell them, Antonina," Ignacy begged, knowing that if his sister became interested in the story of the horse and the czarist police and Kurylowka, she would not urge him to return at once to the house.

"No, you, Ignacy. You know the story as well as I do, and you tell it much better," Antonina answered.

"Well, then," Ignacy began, looking with speculative eyes at Antonina. Was it possible that she could become so engrossed in the story, even though she had heard it many times, that she would forget to urge him to hurry to the house to play the piano? Ignacy hoped so, and decided to make the story very long.

"I was born in the village of Kurylowka," he said, "on the sixth of November in the year 1860. My father was an estate manager there, just as he is here." Ignacy paused, and looked at the faces in front of him. Yes, their owners were set for a long story. He glanced at Antonina and was pleased to see that she had a tender, faraway expression on her face.

"The estate was owned by the Iwanowski family," Ignacy said impressively.

"Our mother died when Ignacy was only a few months old," Antonina said suddenly. "He does not remember her, but I do."

"No, I don't remember her," Ignacy took up the narrative again, "but, like her, I love to play the piano. I've played it since I was three years old. At first, I just used one finger, but by the time I was four I could use all my fingers."

"But tell us about the czarist police," a voice urged.

"He's coming to that," Antonina said, and Ignacy was quick to observe that his sister was absorbed in the story.

"My father played the violin and after he heard me picking out tunes on the piano, he hired a violin teacher to give me piano lessons." Ignacy and all his listeners laughed at this.

17

"That was old Runowski," Antonina said. "He had whiskers and a long beard."

"And couldn't read one note of music," Ignacy said, "but even so, he was a good teacher. Anyway, he was the only musician in the village and our father could not afford to bring a teacher from the city."

Siwek had his head close to Ignacy's as if he, too, were listening to the story. And, indeed, he may have been!

Antonina had no wish to tell the story, but now that her brother had embarked on the whole narrative of their young lives, there were few facts that she wanted overlooked. So now, while Ignacy fed Siwek another cookie, she told their guests that their mother was named Polixena and that she had been the daughter of a professor in the university at Wilno. Then, because Antonina was very loyal to the district of their birth, she described Podole. It was beautiful country, she said, with wide green fields as level as tables and many valleys that were deep and broad.

"I remember that the wheat looked like bands of golden ribbon swaying in the breeze," Antonina said gently. "And something else, I remember, too—the poor little thatched cottages that the people lived in. They were all huddled in the deep valleys by the side of the river. I think they were ashamed to show their ugliness in the bright sunshine of the plains."

"My father says that, though the cottages of Podole were so very poor," Ignacy took up the story here, "there really was a great deal of fruit and grain in the district. But fruit and grain alone will not make people happy. Conditions became very bad in the village and in all the country around.

"One day when I was about four years old," Ignacy said in such an excited voice that his listeners knew that something of great importance was coming, "more than one hundred and fifty Cossacks came to our house. I remember everything that happened that day, I can tell you. Some stayed outside, but many came thumping into the house, where they turned furniture upside down and opened up closets and looked in drawers. In the end, they caught hold of my father and dragged him away."

Ignacy paused and looked about him. Yes, everyone was as eager to hear the next as he was to tell it, he decided, so he continued, "I ran after the Cossacks who held my father, and cried, 'take your hands off my father. Let him go.' Some of them laughed at me, but one burly fellow lifted his whip and lashed me with it."

"Oh! Oh!" the children exclaimed in subdued voices.

"Now, listen! Listen!" Antonina begged.

And everyone did, breathlessly.

"When that big Cossack struck me," Ignacy said, "something very strange happened. The horse that was my pet broke through the crowd of soldiers, and kicked the fellow on the head. In an instant he fell to the ground, and as quickly, the Cossack next to him lifted his rifle and shot my horse dead."

Ignacy's eyes were filled with tears and his lips were trembling. Even though six years had passed since that unhappy time, it was almost like living it all over again to recall it. The children, tears in their eyes, did not know how to show their sympathy, but they and Siwek together drew deep sighs of grief.

"The Cossacks took our father away," Antonina said, "and they burned our house. They did this because our father was a Polish patriot. He was a member of a secret organization that was trying to free Poland from the czar."

"Ah! Ah! Good for him!" some of the children murmured approvingly. In that instant the Polish members of the little gathering liked the Paderewskis even better than before.

"And so our life in Kurylowka ended." Antonina went on with the story while Ignacy searched his pockets for one last cookie for Siwek. "Our aunt came from Nowosiolki, which is near Cudnow, and took us away to live with her. She was often very sick, but even so, she gave us the best of care."

"What did she do?" a village girl, who did not quite understand what "the best care" could mean, asked eagerly.

"Yes, tell us," several called out. It was plain that these Paderewskis had had surprisingly eventful lives.

So Antonina told them that her aunt had engaged a tutor for them, who had taught them to read and write Polish.

"We learned Russian, too," she said, "so that we could write letters to our father in a Russian prison."

"And all the time we both had piano lessons," Ignacy told them. "Never for one day did we miss our practice."

"When our father came from prison, he brought us to Sudylkow, as you know," Antonina said, a tone of finality in her voice, "and ever since we have had Michal Babianski for a tutor."

The story was over. The children looked about them carefully, observing the meadow, the harvest fields, and the houses in the distance. It seemed to the more imaginative ones as if they had just returned to their native land after having been on a long journey.

One boy in the group, after looking from Ignacy to Antonina in a quiet thoughtful way, exclaimed, "How good your father is to you!"

"If my father had money he would be good to us, too," another boy cried out, intense feeling making his voice rough.

Even though she was no more than twelve years old, Antonina Paderewski had an acute instinct for what might be called difficult situations, and she was quick to avoid the possibility of one arising now. "We must go home this instant," she said firmly, and everyone agreed with her.

"They are waiting for you, Ignacy," one and another called out. "The count, you know, and the baron. We forgot all about them."

There was much laughter over this, and Ignacy joined in it, but not Antonina. She could not understand why she had allowed her brother to stay in the meadow for so long. In a flash, she forgot that she had enjoyed the story-telling, and remembered only that Count Chodkiewicz and Baron Horoch must be waiting to hear Ignacy play.

"Hurry! You must hurry," she whispered to her brother. "One of them may help to send you to the conservatory."

"Yes, I know that," Ignacy answered, entirely unperturbed. "I heard that yesterday."

"Papa arranged this party for that very reason," Antonina continued, "and then you hide in the meadow with Siwek and the village children. You are a very careless boy."

But, Ignacy, instead of setting off at top speed, laughed

a little, and reached up to draw Siwek's head down to his. He whispered something into his friend's ear, and was just turning away to follow Antonina when there was the sound of many swiftly galloping feet.

The children stared, fear and horror on their faces. A hundred Cossack soldiers, mounted on sleek horses, were coming over the hill-top and riding toward them. The children stood rigid—glued to the ground. On and on the Cossacks came, and rode past them. Siwek was the only one who watched them ride into the distance, and he neighed and champed his teeth. Every boy and girl knew, without shadow of doubt, that Siwek hated the Cossacks—and their horses.

Ignacy was the first to recover from the fright.

"I'd bet anything that Siwek could throw anyone of those Cossacks from his horse," he said with great pride, "and when he'd done that, he'd grind him up with his teeth. He wouldn't be a Cossack any more."

The children, except Antonina, laughed uproariously at this. She said, "I daresay it's true, Ignacy, but forget about it now. You must hurry. The count and the baron, you know—"

As the children set off for the Paderewski home and the feast that awaited them, several cast anxious, worried glances at the Cossacks, disappearing now into the far distance. Clouds of dust almost hid them from sight.

Two

An Important Concert

Runowski, the old, bearded, and good-natured music teacher, may not have taught Ignacy Paderewski any piano technique, for he played but one instrument, the violin, and that only by ear. Nevertheless, he gave him something of inestimable value. This old man, whose laughter sounded deep and melodious as it came through his thick moustaches, did not know one note of music, but in his heart he had a great and constant love for it. Runowski looked like the image of a saint in a country church and, in spirit, he was like a priest paying tribute to a beloved master. His master was music and in his pupil, Ignacy, Mr. Runowski inculcated the same constant respect and inspired the sacred love that he had himself. Something more he did, and this was of equal importance: he encouraged Mr. Paderewski to educate his son.

"Ignacy has talent, and more, he has genius," he said over and over again to Mr. Paderewski until, finally, the doubting father came to have almost as much confidence in Ignacy's gift as Mr. Runowski had.

Morning after morning, every morning, in fact, the boy went to the living-room and played on the ancient piano given to him by his aunt. The hours lengthened to midday and grew into the afternoon and yet he sat there, playing as he felt. Sometimes the music was loud and stormy, like a tempest; sometimes it was soft and gentle as raindrops tapping on a window-pane. His childish hopes and fears, his affection, his confidence—his whole life—were poured out in rhythmic sound.

When he was seven a new teacher came to give Ignacy piano lessons. He was Piotr Sowinski; but Mr. Sowinski, although he had an extensive education in music, did not play the piano well. In those days it was most difficult to secure a pianist as a teacher, and even if one could have been found, Ignacy's father would not have been able to pay the fee, for he was far from being rich.

However, Mr. Sowinski had something to teach his two young pupils. He taught them the theory of music and he set them many exercises. He held Italian music in high esteem, so he introduced Antonina and Ignacy to the operas of Donizetti, Rossini, and other Italian musicians. They spent many hours playing "Il Barbiere," or "Lucia di Lammermoor," and "Norma." They used to play together, Ignacy always in the low notes.

This teaching satisfied Antonina, perhaps, but not Ignacy.

He became impatient with a teacher who could not instruct him in any of the essential technique of piano playing. How could his genius, of which he had so often heard Mr. Runow-ski speak, develop if his teacher could not play the piano?

Piotr Sowinski was almost as astute as his young pupil and, in an endeavor to compensate for his music deficiency, he approached Count Chodkiewicz and later, Baron Horoch. He interested them in Ignacy Paderewski's remarkable gift, and they, finally, agreed to assist his father in sending him to the conservatory in Warszawa.

With the willingness of the count and baron achieved, only part of the battle was won. Mr. Paderewski had to be persuaded anew that his son's talent was worthy of this great undertaking. His first protest was that he could not afford to pay his son's maintenance in the city for a period extending into years. His next one concerned Antonina. She deserved as much as her brother and he could not give it to her, since he had to assist some of his wife's relatives, who had been deported to Siberia because of their activities in a secret Polish patriotic organization. There was another reason for Mr. Paderewski's reluctance: his term in the czar's prison had left a bad mark on his health. His sight was failing slowly and steadily and he needed his son beside him to read papers and documents for him. This last perplexity—how to do his work without Ignacy to help him—he did not express to the count and the baron, nor to Piotr Sowinski, aided now in his persuasion by the wise tutor of the two children, Mr. Babianski.

While the decision as to whether he was to go to Warszawa or not was being weighed in the balance, Ignacy was by no means wasting his time. When he was not playing the piano in the large parlor with the striped red and gold carpet, he was riding over the countryside with Siwek or playing games with the barefooted and ragged children of Sudylkow. Gradually he had less time for Siwek, for invitations to play the piano at parties were increasing. Almost every Sunday he and Antonina went somewhere to play at feasts and parties. They must have travelled hundreds of miles and for as many hours during this eventful year and, though the remuneration was high in praise and fame, it was not in money, for most of these feasts were arranged for charity.

Every invitation and every performance excited Ignacy. He loved the applause people gave them, and sometimes he must have marvelled at Antonina's quiet indifference to it. Even while people talked of the great musical gift of the two young Paderewskis, she would sit calmly by the fire, looking at the pictures in a book or sewing a seam in a shirt for one of the poor. But not Ignacy. He glowed, and with every plaudit promised even greater demonstrations of their talent. Filled with this enthusiasm, his ambition grew, not only for himself but for Antonina, too. He played constantly; he thought of nothing, it seemed, but the majestic piano and the music that he could draw from its black and white keys. Whether the room was flooded with sunshine or lighted by the pale light of the candelabra did not matter—he played with unflagging enthusiasm.

Before he was twelve, Ignacy Paderewski gave a concert in the provincial town of Zaslaw. A short time later, on the eve of his twelfth birthday, he had his second concert, this time in the beautiful, old city of Ostrog in Wolyn. It was this concert that decided his departure for Warszawa. Something of even more consequence resulted from the visit to Ostrog.

It was nearly four o'clock in the afternoon. Count Chodkiewicz's party, which included Mr. Babianski, Ignacy Paderewski, and his stepmother, was approaching the ancient city from the east. The gray walls of a prince's castle loomed darkly in the far distance and the tall towers and spire of a church looked like slender black ladders mounted in the glowing sky. The polished brass trimmings of the four horses' harnesses caught the sun's bright rays and shone with double brilliance. Ignacy Paderewski was sitting in the front seat of the first carriage of the little cavalcade. Count Chodkiewicz and Mr. Babianski were in the back seat, while Ignacy's stepmother and the Baroness Horoch were in a second carriage a few paces behind. Ignacy had alert ears and the light breezes assisted him in picking up bits of the conversation of the count and the teacher.

"There is no doubt about it," the count said, "the boy is talented. The whole countryside is talking of him, and no wonder either, for he has good manners as well as a gift. Yes, he'll be a pianist of the first order."

It was easy to see that the count was turning an idea that concerned Ignacy Paderewski over and over in his mind. The listener in the front seat almost bent backward in an effort to hear everything.

"Not of a pianist, but a composer, too," Mr. Babianski was quick to say. "He has started composing. His father has shown me his notebooks. Mazurkas and polonaises chiefly."

"Then why, when the boy has so much promise, does the father hesitate?" the count asked. "Surely he knows that Ignacy should be attending the conservatory in Warszawa."

"He realizes it," Babianski answered thoughtfully, "but he can't bring himself to consent. He is worried about money, for one thing. His wife is not well and she may need a doctor. Her people depend on him for help, and, besides, there is Antonina. Mr. Paderewski wants her to have educational privileges, too."

"To be sure! To be sure! I can understand that," the count said impatiently.

"After all, as his father says, Ignacy is young yet. Only twelve, you know, and that's pretty young for leaving home and going to a big city like Warszawa." To hear him, one would have thought that Mr. Babianski was on Mr. Paderewski's side.

"Well, for my part, I think he's wrong, absolutely wrong," the count said with great emphasis. "The boy is young, yes, but he has genius. He could become a celebrated musician, and, as everyone knows, a musical education should be started early. As early as possible."

Mr. Babianski drew a deep sigh of agreement. There was a long silence. Ignacy, blushing now and anxious to appear as if he had heard nothing, asked the coachman if he could drive the horses.

"If Jan Paderewski is really faced with financial difficulties, I might be willing to finance his son's education," the count said very slowly and impressively.

The listener in the front seat had to put his hand over his mouth to smother an exclamation of joy.

"Everyone talks of the boy's gifts," Babianski said, "but until this moment absolutely no one has suggested how they should be developed. Runowski said Warszawa, but he didn't say how. Sowinski said the same, but nothing more. His aunt, his grandmother, yes, and even I—we've all chatted and chatted—but now you come along and say, 'I'll do it.' Wonderful!"

The teacher was pleased with the count and the count could not restrain his delight in himself.

"Yes, I'll do it," he said resolutely, "and we'll begin right now. For me, the best time for anything is immediately. Ignacy shall go to the conservatory this year, but first I shall take him to Kiev. What do you think of that, Babianski? Kiev, first, aye?" The count twisted his long moustaches, and looked at Babianski for approval.

But Mr. Babianski did not approve. He looked thoughtfully into the distance and when he spoke, at last, his voice rang with passion.

"Why should Ignacy, a Polish boy, go to Kiev?" he demanded. "Warszawa is the capital of Poland. It has a famous conservatory. He should go there, even though our country is in chains, instead of going to a czarist city. He should get to know Polish culture; that is his natural right."

Mr. Babianski, like Ignacy's father, had suffered exile, and had returned to his native land only a short time before he became tutor to the Paderewski children. He knew the power and the subversive quality of the czar's whip.

Count Chodkiewicz was scornful. He shook a finger in Mr. Babianski's face as he said, "You must curb that wild tongue of yours, my friend, or you'll find yourself in Siberia again. Don't think I haven't seen you talking in whispers with Polish revolutionaries, for I have."

Mr. Babianski was disturbed. Would he never learn, he asked himself, to think his thoughts but not speak them?

The count returned to the main subject of their discussion, after first saying, "Anyway, don't worry too much, Babianski. Warszawa will soon be Poland's capital once more. The revolutionists are working all over the country." He laughed a little sarcastically as he said this.

"Now about Ignacy. I shall take him to Kiev with me next week. After all, it is not a Russian city, as you seem to think, but Ukrainian. It will be good for the boy to see a beautiful, dignified old city. I shall take him to the theater and the opera. He can attend a real concert." The count was becoming very enthusiastic about this project of educating Mr. Jan Paderewski's gifted son.

Ignacy, perched high on the front seat with the driver, had not missed a word. The kind wind had brought him each one and dropped it into his eager ears. Next week! So soon! He was to go to Kiev! He was so excited he could hardly breathe. He stood up in his seat, and clapped the reins on the horses' backs so vigorously that the driver, whom he had wakened from a drowsy sleep, took the reins from him and muttered a vigorous admonition. But Ignacy did not care. He was going to Kiev and next to Warszawa. Count Chodkiewicz had said so. There could be no doubt about it.

Let them go on talking if they liked, Mr. Babianski and the count, but nothing they might say mattered much to Ignacy now. For him the conversation was over. He turned his attention to Ostrog, which they had just entered. As their carriage rattled over its bumpy cobbled streets, he looked at the people, and wondered if this one and that would be at his concert. There were many long-bearded Jewish merchants wearing stained black jackets. There were many country women with brightly colored kerchiefs on their heads and wearing full skirts that fell almost to their bare feet. Those people who had on shoes, Ignacy decided, must be rich merchants or noblemen. He saw it all—the once rich city with its crumbling gray walls making a background for the colorful panorama of people—and to the boy it seemed as if the whole populace, Jews, country women, and well-shod noblemen, were making ready for a great festive occasion, and that occasion was his concert.

"I will play for these people as I have never played before," Ignacy promised himself, "and they'll stare at me with bright eyes and open mouths, and when it is over they will say that I am wonderful. 'Greatly gifted,' that's what they'll say."

In that great moment of anticipation and exaltation, Ignacy Paderewski envisaged an audience of many thousands crowded on rows and rows of benches—so many benches that he could not see the last ones from his place on the platform. And such melody as would stream from his strong young fingers. . . .

In actual fact, about a hundred people gathered in a small hall to hear the youthful prodigy play. The compensation for so small an audience was slight and one that Ignacy did not greatly appreciate. The people were the cream of the country-side. They were the friends and relatives of the Baron Horoch and Count Chodkiewicz, with the result that some of the most illustrious people in all Poland were there. The Chodkiewicz family had through all history taken an important place in their country's affairs, particularly as military leaders and knights.

Ignacy's stepmother sat in the front row with the aristocrats of the first order. She was nervous, naturally, and cast many anxious glances toward the dressing-room where Mr. Babianski was busy preparing the boy for his entrance to the stage. He brushed his golden hair and dusted his slightly crumpled suit, all the time whispering words of encouragement to him, for now, as the great moment approached, Ignacy lost his confidence. He wished, helplessly, that his father were there, but Mr. Paderewski had been detained at home because of his onerous duties on the estate. Not even to hear his gifted son play before an illustrious audience, would he leave his work of supervising the laborers on the farm. He was truly a remarkable individual, this elder Paderewski, as loyal to his master and as diligent in his service as his young son was to music and the piano. A favorite saying of his was, "when you have a horse, it is your duty to feed him," which, in reality, meant when one has a position, it is his responsibility to see that all the work it entails is done.

From wishing for his father, Ignacy turned his thoughts to Antonina. If only she could have been with him! She was so calm and self-possessed. Just to look at her quiet, smiling face, was to have courage and assurance. But Antonina had had to stay at home because she had a cold and coughed very much. So except for Mr. Babianski's support, Ignacy was put upon his own resources of self-control. He walked to and fro in the little dressing-room, which was the caretaker's office as well, and waited for his "call." It came after a man had played the violin and a woman, a relative of the Baron Horoch, had sung.

"Now then! Now then!" Mr. Babianski exclaimed suddenly. "It's your turn. Go now, Ignacy, and play. Play better than you have ever done."

Without hesitation, his music clutched in his hand, Ignacy ran to the stage and was greeted by enthusiastic applause. He liked that. It showed that already he was known in this Wolyn community. He made the ceremonious bow that his step-mother and Mr. Babianski had taught him, and began playing. First he played a short piece from Tedesco, and followed it with something by Kalkbrenner, two composers who were popular at that time.

The applause was like red apples falling into his lap. He loved it, and showed his appreciation in a boyish manner that pleased his audience.

Next "Il Barbiere" flowed from his fingers and it was followed by the "Carnival of Venice." He played like a madman. It seemed to him, as the music reverberated through the hall, that all the world must dance to the music he was drawing from his piano. If the composers could have heard their music on that night, they, surely, would have been astonished by their achievements. The young artist played with intense feeling; he played only as one who understands can play. When Ignacy finished the middle group of his repertoire, and bowed in response to the applause, he saw a smile of deep satisfaction on the face of Count Chodkiewicz.

Ignacy Paderewski finished his concert with several Chopin mazurkas. He played them well, he knew from the audience's approval.

"I must play them better, though, much better," he whispered to himself, as he stood alone on the stage, "and I will. Much better. I'll charm the world with these mazurkas." His brief soliloquy was the eager ambition of an artist, not the prophecy of a seer.

When the concert was over, Ignacy received the commendations of his listeners with the grace of a poised and experienced musician. "Next time I shall do better," he said with pride. "Chopin is difficult, yes, but I will practise."

When the Count Chodkiewicz shook his hand, he whispered, "My child, I am going to take you to Kiev. You will go to the opera and to concerts. Very soon, now, we shall go. Next week, without fail."

And Ignacy, pretending that he had heard not one word of the conversation in the carriage, showed surprise as well as delight.

Soon he was in the carriage again, in the back seat this time, sitting beside his stepmother, and soon he was asleep, his head, his very tired head, pillowed on her breast. He was weary, so weary, like a hare that has been chased by the hounds, but, at last, has eluded them. He slept and dreamed as the heavy carriage jolted through the dark night, and his dream was a strange mingling of the concert and his ambitions for the future. The golden and silvery spires of Kiev churches, for Kiev was famous for its churches; concert halls, crowded with smiling, richly dressed people; Warszawa, his country's capital, despite the czar's ordinances; his father with tears in his eyes, bidding him Godspeed—and there were other pictures, not wholly distinguishable in the thin white mist of his dream.

The great carriage trundled on and Ignacy stirred. In that pleasant state between sleep and waking, he recalled the lines in Slowacki's poem, *Anhelli,* that described fields covered with snow and the wanderings of the hero. He had read those lines so often, sometimes to himself, but more frequently to his father.

Snowy fields, dangers, obstacles—how Anhelli had fought and struggled to free his fatherland from the chains of slavery! As Ignacy rubbed his eyes and sat up straight, this thought ran through his mind: his father was like Anhelli. He had suffered imprisonment in Siberia because he had tried to win freedom for Poland, and now his health was failing. His sight was growing dim. In that moment, Ignacy Paderewski became aware of the battle that was being fought and had been fought by Polish heroes.

Three

The Road from Kiev

A few months had passed since the concert at Ostrog. Count Chodkiewicz had kept his promise to take the young pianist to Kiev.

Like a stealthy enemy creeping on an unwitting foe, the darkness of night closed in on the broad, snow-covered fields. The tall trees of the forest, standing as a bulwark behind the fields, swayed and creaked in the winter's wind. The sound had the threat of danger. A queer other-world crackle rose from the ice-encrusted earth and other strange noises mingled with it. Perhaps they were the complaints of human beings caught in the wind's cold blasts. Perhaps they were the pitiful wails of forest animals, raised in a prayer for the release that spring could bring them. But whatever the sounds—all were smothered by the metallic ring of well-shod horses' hoofs and the shrill, high notes of sleigh-bells, and all were blended into one powerful symphony that rolled and echoed through the night. It would have been easy to give the clear, turbulent music a title; it could have been called "The Cry of Ukrainia," for that country, like Poland, suffered under the czar's yoke of slavery.

Ignacy Paderewski was in a sleigh that was being carried along the snowy road, and no sound of the night escaped his listening ears. He sat beside the Baron Horoch, completely absorbed in the music of the night. For him the forest was singing; the fields were singing; all the world was singing; and he had a vision of an orchestra playing the full, clear melodies. An orchestra, and he, Ignacy Paderewski, would be in that orchestra; all the other members would, in fact, be around him. He wished that he were at home, at this moment, writing down every sound of the symphony that was filling his ears. The music rose and swelled again—to the very sky, the young pianist thought, where, behind the deep blue, billowy clouds of night, were hidden the secrets of to-morrow. Would the long, long road from Kiev to Sudylkow never come to an end, he wondered impatiently?

The sleigh, drawn by four prancing bay horses, glided swiftly over the well-packed snow. The driver, sitting erect on the box above his passengers, showed no sign of being afraid of the cold, but Ignacy and the fat baron cowered under black sheepskin blankets. All that the driver could see when he turned to look at them were their noses, and he chuckled to himself, "Frozen, no doubt," and stopped his horses. He climbed down from his perch and brought snow. "Rub," he ordered each of his passengers in turn, and pointed to the white, frost-bitten noses.

A second sleigh trundled noisily behind the first one. It was piled high with baggage and the driver, Kierylo, shouted constantly to his horses to keep pace with their leaders.

Count Chodkiewicz and his family had been in the party when it had gone from Sudylkow to Kiev, but they were not returning now. They had grown weary of country life and were staying in the Ukrainian city for a longer holiday. Ignacy thought of this for a few moments, and marvelled at it. He had no idea what being weary might be; he had never experienced it, and certainly he was not likely to in Sudylkow, for he played the piano there, sometimes for whole days at a time with only a few pauses for food. He wrote down snatches of melodies that surged through his head until his pile of notebooks was now very high and very wide. He loved Sudylkow; this much he had found out when he was homesick in Kiev; it meant home and work to him and he loved both. Not that he had not liked Kiev. It had been a thrilling holiday, the more so, perhaps, because it was his first experience of a big city.

The museums, for instance, and the libraries. He had never known before that there were so many paintings and statues and books in the world. And the churches, convents, and monasteries—there were so many and all were magnificent with gleaming altars and icons and colorful portrayals of scenes from the life of Christ. It would take him days to describe them all to Antonina.

Then there were the people on the street. He would have to tell her about the bearded Jews dressed in long black satin coats that were worn and even in tatters. And about the burghers who looked poorer than the peasants at Sudylkow. But he would take the longest time in describing the opera and the concerts, for there he had seen throngs of czarist officers in gold-braided uniforms and their chests ablaze with medals. The women's gowns had been so amazing that he doubted his ability to describe them. The Baroness Horoch had tried to help him by telling him that the rich cloth was either brocade or velvet and that the jewels, that sparkled and gleamed and looked like multitudes of brightly-burning fires, were diamonds. She had drawn his attention to several famous pearl necklaces, but he knew he would not be able to tell Antonina about their lustrous beauty.

And how would he ever be able to tell her of the artists? Their voices had been soft like gently-flowing brooks; they had been clear like church bells ringing and deep like thunder growing louder and louder. The Beethoven concert, he was sure, would stay longer in his memory than any other. The powerful music had swept him away entirely from his surroundings. For two hours, at least, he had lived in the music of the great master.

Antonina, he knew, would love his account of the great singer, Adelaide Ristori. They had read about her beautiful voice, and now he had seen and heard her. Would Antonina laugh when he told her that he had begged Count Chodkiewicz to introduce him to her? Surely not. She would sympathize with him when he would tell her that the count had not succeeded in presenting him because Madame Ristori had had to rush from the opera to catch a train to Moscow. Next, he would tell her what the Countess Chodkiewicz had said when she had seen his disappointment.

"In five or ten years, my little golden kitten, the Madam Ristori will be begging for an introduction to you," the countess had said, patting his hand and smiling a very knowing smile.

This had been poor comfort to Ignacy. Indeed, it had done little more than remind him of his dislike of his long, golden hair.

As the sleigh jolted into deep ruts in the road, he began to think of his home and of the welcome his father would give him. His next thoughts were of his immediate future. He would not stay in Sudylkow for long, he knew.

"Shall I go to Kiev or Warszawa to study?" he asked himself, and continued the one-sided discussion with, "I would prefer Kiev. There are many artists and teachers there, more probably than in Warszawa. But my father, I know, will want me to go to Warszawa. 'Enslaved or not, Warszawa is always the capital of our country,' is what he will say, 'and it is better, my son, for you to be educated and punished by your own people.'"

A tender little smile flickered on the boy's face as he thought of his father, and recalled the words he had so often heard him say. His father was a patriot, and so was he, Ignacy, but music came even before patriotism. Yes, it did. Right or wrong, his ambition to be a great musician surpassed his resolution to be a Polish patriot. Ever since he was three years old, his mind and heart had hungered for music; it was a hunger that gave him no peace. Wherever he went, he heard and felt strange, haunting melodies. In the fields of Wolyn. In the forest when he roamed with Siwek. In Kiev when he saw the poor burghers, and watched the brilliantly dressed audience gathering in the concert hall. Everywhere. He was nearly twelve, and he knew, without shadow of a doubt, that music was to be his life. The world to him was music. The happenings of a single day were music. Everything.

Suddenly an eerie sound rang through the forest. It was neither a moan nor a roar. It was strange, weird, frightening. Ignacy shivered. The horses leapt into a run. The driver shouted, "Wolves! Wolves!" and lashed his horses with a whip. The baron and Ignacy threw back their sheepskin blankets, and sat up straight in their seats. The sharp wind whistled and poured shrill noises into their ears. The hungry, cruel cries of wolves—these were the sounds that burdened the wind.

"Look! Look!" the baron cried. "There to the right, see them, the ugly brutes. They are coming towards us."

"We have no time to lose," the driver shouted and lashed his galloping horses again.

"What are we going to do?" Ignacy asked, his lips quivering.

"You'll see," the baron answered, and began waving his arms to Kierylo, who brought his horses alongside those of the baron in a few minutes.

Without either a command being given or an enquiry made, Kierylo began throwing the pieces of luggage from his sleigh into the baron's. And all the time both teams of horses were tearing over the road at almost breakneck speed. The wolves came nearer and nearer. Now they were very near, and Ignacy held his breath. He was terrified.

What came next? What? Kierylo knew. He leapt from his

driver's box to the back of his leading horse. The instant he was out of the sleigh, the baron stood up, took a bundle of straw from the floor of his sleigh, lighted a match to it, and flung it into Kierylo's sleigh. By this time Kierylo had unhitched his horses from the burning sleigh. And with not an instant to lose either, for now the wolves were beside the burning vehicle. Ignacy looked back, and in the flame's glow, saw them standing still. Mournful bays rolled out on the clear night air. The wolves were angry at being defeated and some other quality was mingled in their howls. Fear? Yes, fear, Ignacy thought, and asked the baron.

"You are right," he answered as he wiped perspiration from his brow. "Wolves are afraid of fire."

"It was wonderful," Ignacy exclaimed exultantly. "I was so frightened, I couldn't do a thing, but you knew exactly what to do, didn't you, Baron Horoch?"

"As I should, for I have had much experience with timber wolves," the baron answered, then added, "But it was not I so much as Kierylo. He acted without one moment's hesitation."

Kierylo lifted his head from the cup of vodka the baron had poured for him, and smiled from one to the other. "The next time wolves set upon you, Master Paderewski, you'll know exactly what to do," he said.

The baron and Ignacy wrapped themselves in their blankets again. Soon the former was asleep, as his deep rumbling snores proclaimed, and Ignacy had resumed the course of his thoughts. Very soon, now, he would be at home and his father would be talking to him of his future.

"I'll go to the conservatory in Warszawa," Ignacy murmured

Ignacy Paderewski, at fifteen, with his father

to himself, "and I'll listen to every word of advice he gives me before I go. After all, he should be able to tell me how to conduct myself among strangers, for he knows the world."

The picture that he conjured up before his eyes was of a boy, himself, standing on a railroad station platform. There was a little bag of spending money in one of his pockets and a letter of introduction to one of his father's friends in Warszawa in another pocket. It was a moving picture, for the boy was being kissed by his stepmother and his sister, both of them with tears in their eyes, and his father was opening the train carriage door for him. At last—the train got up steam; it puff-puffed away on its journey, and the boy, leaning far out, waved farewell.

For a few minutes Ignacy listened to the conversation of the two drivers. The wind carried their words to him clearly, and he was glad the baron was asleep. He would not have wanted him to have overheard what they were saying. Yet why shouldn't he? They were talking of their wives who had to work hard and of their children who were clever, but who, without doubt, would have to work as herdsmen and maid-servants on the estate of some count or baron. Ignacy's heart leapt for joy when he heard Kierylo say that the day was coming when common people would be able to have their sons and daughters educated.

"And we shall not have to go begging to our titled land-owners," Kierylo said with conviction.

Another dream-picture flitted before Ignacy: a young musician seated at a piano, and as far as his eyes could see, the happy countenances of a pleased audience. The melody that the musician was drawing from the piano came to his ears, faint, at first, but as the night gave birth to the dawn, it became clear and full and beautiful. The steppes of Ukrainia were far behind. They had disappeared with the night and the wolves and the burning sleigh. An unknown day was coming to the world. It was coming, especially to Ignacy Jan Paderewski.

Four

At the Conservatory in Warszawa

On the very day Ignacy Paderewski arrived in Warszawa, he began the most essential parts of his musical training at the conservatory. He was ready to study hard, and started lectures in harmony and counterpoint under Professor Roguski who had been trained by the famous Berlioz. The theory of music was taught by Professor Studzinski; and both masters, Roguski and Studzinski, soon prophesied a career as composer for the boy from Sudylkow. Professor Roguski, especially, took a deep and constant interest in him. He became his friend and adviser, and soon Ignacy was seeking him out daily for discussions and opinions, not only on the subject of harmony, but on the general course of his life. Professor Roguski's confidence in him supported and comforted Ignacy when his heart was heavy with homesickness and when he became discouraged.

He was so eager to realize his heart's desire and so willing to pour out his whole being—spirit, mind, and body—in the great effort. And everywhere he went in Warszawa, his country's capital, he found sources of inspiration. The conservatory itself, for instance. Here, within these ancient walls, many famous musicians had been trained. In Ignacy's enthusiastic opinion, the greatest of all these was Chopin. He, Ignacy Jan Paderewski, was walking along the same corridors as had resounded to the quick footsteps of the youthful Chopin. He was sitting in the same lecture halls, handling the same scripts of music, gazing at the same pictures, reading the same books.

Another thought that was often in his mind as he walked to and from the conservatory, and paused often to look at its stately structure, was this institution that had lifted its head above the shame the czar had put upon it. After the Polish people had risen in revolt against their overlords in 1831, the czar had ordered the conservatory of Warszawa abolished and the building to be used as a storehouse for firearms. For twenty-nine years the city bore this insult, but in 1860 permission had been granted to open the doors of the conservatory again to its music-loving young people.

When Ignacy Paderewski registered at the conservatory, he commenced the study of the flute. He did not like it and turned to the oboe. As that pleased him no better, he was given permission to try the bassoon. The result was so discouraging that he was assigned to the horn. In all these weeks of experiment and discouragement, he barely touched the piano. His fingers ached for the keyboard and his heart was sick for the throb of his chosen instrument.

At last there came a day of bitter argument and firm command. The director of the conservatory school, Apolinary Kontski, a violinist of repute, sent for him, and said that he expected him to play regularly in the school orchestra. It was as if a bomb had exploded at Ignacy's feet and covered him with bits of his shattered hopes. Play the horn regularly! Never! And Ignacy spoke his resolution furiously. The director was not one whit less resolute.

"I came here to learn to play the piano," Ignacy stormed, "not to play a horn instrument in the school orchestra."

The director glared at the boy, stamped his feet, twisted his moustache, and shouted, "You will not do what I, the director, tell you? Then you are expelled. Expelled for disobedience."

This happened in the year 1875, and it was like a heavy black curtain being drawn down on the hopes and career of Ignacy Paderewski. Someone must help him, but to whom could he turn? Not to Professor Roguski. He was ashamed and his pride would not let him go to his friend.

He moped in his room for days. At this time he was boarding in the home of the Kerntopf family, well-known makers of pianos, and at last, Edward Kerntopf, eldest son of the family, observed the boy's misery. It did not take much urging to draw the story of his misfortune from Ignacy, and it did not take young Mr. Kerntopf long to decide what should be done. He would write a letter to the director, a simple, frank letter in which he would admit that Ignacy was a hot-tempered boy. Hot-tempered but studious. Very studious. Edward Kerntopf said other things in the letter, too: that Ignacy had proven

49

long before he came to the conservatory that he had great talent for the piano; that his father, Kerntopf, the maker of pianos, had prophesied that Ignacy would some day be a great pianist.

A few weeks later Ignacy returned to the conservatory, this time as a student of the piano. Being expelled had so shocked him that when he returned, with his heart's desire granted, he applied himself with even greater diligence. He had need of his diligence and the courage that came to him with his constant application to the piano, for his instructors were almost unanimous in telling him that he would not be a great pianist. Professor Sliwinski was his first teacher, and after him came Schlozer, Strobel, and Janoth; and of the four, Professor Strobel was the only one who expressed any confidence in Ignacy's qualities as a pianist. As a composer—ah yes, they thought so; but as an interpreter—it was doubtful.

There were times when his courage was not high enough to support his confidence. He could feel music surging through him and yet—would he never be able to interpret his deep feelings? Sometimes it was as if grief smothered his spirit. But not for long; his spirit was resilient; the will to achieve was a constant flame in him.

The greatest friendliness he had in these first days in Warszawa was shown him by the Kerntopf family. Old Madam Kerntopf treated him like a member of her household, and Edward watched over him the way one would over a young brother. Edward's sister had similar affection for him, and frequently the two of them went on long walks into the country. She was a willing and attentive listener, so Ignacy poured out his great ambitions to her. At other times they discussed music and the careers of famous musicians.

Many famous musicians and artists visited the Kerntopf family; it was in their hospitable home that Ignacy first met the celebrated pianist, Nicholas Rubinstein, and the Polish composers, Wieniawski, Zelenski, and Noskowski. On several never-to-be-forgotten occasions Theodor Leschetizky, the renowned teacher of the piano, and his wife, the concert pianist, Essipoff, came from Vienna to spend holidays in the Kerntopf household. Perhaps the visitor who delighted the youthful Paderewski most was Kazimiertz Hoffmann who would play Chopin by the hour. Ignacy drank in the music, and at the same time watched the expressions on the faces of the listeners. Sometime—soon, surely—he would delight music-loving people, even as Hoffmann was doing now.

Another privilege that came to him while he was with the Kerntopf's was going to the opera. Edward Kerntopf received complimentary tickets from the director, Adam Munchheimer, and he frequently invited Ignacy to accompany him. It was at the opera in Warszawa that he learned to love Verdi, especially his *Aida;* and soon he began patterning his trial operas on those of the Italian composer.

It was during this time that he started going to the theatre. While he was a student at the conservatory, so he said later, he never missed a performance of the Polish actress, Helena Modrzejewska. Once after he had seen her in Shakespeare's *Othello,* he persuaded Edward Kerntopf to give a reception for the two great artists of the stage, Modrzejewska and Leszczynski. It was at this sumptuous function, which was by far the most magnificent Ignacy had attended, that his friendship with Modrzejewska began. It lasted throughout her life.

However, hearing and seeing artists was not enough for Ignacy Paderewski. He became impatient with himself and the life he was living. He wanted to prove himself a musician. He wanted to see his name on billboards and in press announcements and, almost as important, he wanted to make money. When he found that his friends Biernacki and Cielewicz had similar ambitions, the three made a pact to give concerts. Biernacki would play the cello, Cielewicz the violin, and Paderewski, naturally, the piano. Neither his father nor the Baron Horoch and Count Chodkiewicz showed much enthusiasm for the proposal, as was revealed by the reluctant manner in which they contributed roubles for the venture. There were days when Ignacy, waiting for engagements, had no money whatever in his pocket—or he would not have had if one or other member of the Kerntopf family had not slipped money into it. Madam Kerntopf insisted that he continue to live with them and take his meals with the family, even if he could not pay his board.

This generosity tortured Ignacy. He thought sometimes that he could endure hunger better than their kindness. His indebtedness was mounting. He decided that he must pay—now, at once—and so, without much thought he made a decision. Rather, three persons—Biernacki, Cielewicz, and Paderewski—made a decision. They would go on a concert tour. They would go north through Poland and into Russia and when they were rich, they would return, triumphant, to

Warszawa. The seventeen-year old Ignacy was afire with eagerness.

They set off with hopes soaring like larks into the distant blue sky. They went from one city to another. Each gave promise of being better than the last one, but alas, it was a promise that was never fulfilled. Riches did not flow to them like rivers to the sea. Roubles came slowly and in such tiny sums that they had barely money enough for food and travelling expenses. This did not dampen their buoyant spirits, however, and they roamed on, until their families discovered their whereabouts and commanded them to return home. Biernacki and Cielewicz then admitted that they had had enough, but not Paderewski. He went on to St. Petersburg alone.

Grim misfortune overtook him in the strange Russian city. He became ill, and as if that were not suffering enough, all his belongings were stolen, including a hundred roubles his father had sent him for the express purpose of buying a railroad ticket to Sudylkow. Well, perhaps the thief needed the money. Perhaps he was homesick for his home and his family, just as young Paderewski was.

Ignacy was so worn out from his strenuous travelling and for want of nourishing food, that he could not throw off the illness. He was living in the home of a poor railroad worker in St. Petersburg and the man's wife took pity on him when she saw how sick he was. She bathed his hot face and hands, and put compresses of cold cloths on his head. Still the fever was slow in abating. One night when he had tossed and turned on his board bed, and mumbled incoherently for hours, he dropped suddenly into a light sleep. The housewife, watching him, marvelled at the happiness that spread over his face.

"He is having a dream, perhaps of his home and his childhood," she whispered to her husband.

A dream, he was having, but not of his home. It was of a hundred roubles, a second hundred. He heard his father being told of the theft of the first hundred, and saw him sending another hundred. The very next day the dream came true. A letter that had been following him from one city to another caught up with him, at last, in the humble laborer's home in St. Petersburg and a package of roubles tumbled out. How good his father was to him! It did not take him long to recover, and soon he was on his way back to Warszawa and his studies.

There is no short cut to fame; Ignacy Paderewski knew this well as he made his way back to the conservatory. Talent one must have, to be sure, but that talent, if it is to burn like an undying flame, must be fed by constant work. The two together are the key to success. The two together produce mastery, even genius, and Ignacy Paderewski was convinced of this elemental truth when he returned to Warszawa. On this ill-fated concert tour he had learned one of the greatest lessons of his life.

Five

Tosia and a New World of Music

"He is through with his studies at the conservatory. My son is graduating with honors, just as he promised me he would do. He will be a great musician. He has his diploma now." These thoughts and many others concerning his son, Ignacy, ran in a procession through Mr. Jan Paderewski's head, as he sat in a great hall in Warszawa.

He glanced frequently with smiling eyes at the young girl sitting by his side, and murmured, "Ah, it is good, very good. You will see. He will be a famous musician, our Ignacy."

Each time he whispered this happy assurance, the girl nodded her head in agreement. This, to her, was the happiest day of her life. For her, the vast hall did not exist; neither did the throng of people, even though pleasure was revealed in all their faces. The young musician and the music that rolled from the piano made a full and wonderful world for her. The music rolled and echoed through the hall, poured in a constant torrent from the windows and the doors, and reverberated through the streets. It was magnificent, this playing of Ignacy Paderewski on the day of his graduation.

For him, too, this was the happiest day of his life. He was graduating, and the two persons who were dearest to him in all the world were listening to him play. One was his old father, more than half blind now, but happy despite his growing affliction. Many times in years to come, he would recall the joyous expression that glowed on his father's face on this day. The other person was his sweetheart, Antonina Korsak, who was sitting with his father, and whose bright face and generous, loving character were to be the inspiration of some of his best work. In the future whenever he recalled this day, he would remember Antonina's eager young face, her shining hair, and the soft blue of her lace frock. Hard years, years of loneliness and persistent work were to come, years that he would study and starve and struggle in Berlin, but there would always be the memory of this day when his father and Antonina had sat together, listening to him play his farewell to his studies at the conservatory in Warszawa.

The last chords of Chopin died away. The graduation was over. Gentle thoughts, eager thoughts, and thoughts tinged ever so slightly with regret, surged up in Ignacy Paderewski, but in a flash they all flowed together into an engulfing rush of ambitious plans for the future.

The year was 1879, and already Ignacy Paderewski had had one of his compositions published. It was entitled "Impromptu in F Major," and it had been issued by the publisher, W. Banarski. He had dedicated this selection to the man who had maintained confidence in his gifts as a pianist, Professor Strobel. Despite the dedication, Ignacy knew that he had written this music for no one but Tosia Korsak. It was gay and reckless, even though a note of melancholy stole into it at times. Yes, it really belonged to Tosia.

In the year 1880, Antonina, or Tosia as she was called by her friends, and Ignacy were married. In roubles they were poor, but their poverty went no further. In love they were millionaires. In ambition they were very, very rich. And in golden dreams of the future. They took a house and both began to teach music, Ignacy at the conservatory where he had had so many unhappy experiences, and Antonina in their home. In addition, Ignacy gave a few private lessons, and the steady sale of the "Impromptu" helped them to maintain their little household. Many well-known pianists in Vienna and Moscow were already including his music in their programmes. Yes, indeed, the world was good; the city of Warszawa was good. Ignacy and Tosia Paderewski were so happy that they felt that the great city and the world beyond was theirs. And so it would have been, if joy and hope and youthful ambition could have been the purchase price.

With Tosia to work for and Tosia to encourage him, Ignacy felt that he could accomplish everything. Nothing could be too difficult. In a few short years the world would know him as a pianist and a composer. They shared one certainty, these two confident lovers—that Ignacy would gain eternal fame.

Tosia had, of course, received a dowry from her parents, and to this she kept adding her earnings as a teacher—and all for one important purpose. Ignacy was to have the money to take him to Berlin and Vienna, perhaps even to Italy, to study under the world's most renowned teachers.

"Soon, now, very soon," she would say to him, "and you will be able to go over the border to Berlin."

When he would protest his use of "you" and say "we" instead, she would shake her head and answer, "No! No, you, only. I shall stay here and teach music. You will need all our roubles for lessons. Then when the year is over, you will come home and we shall go together to the Tatry Mountains for a holiday."

Ignacy was reluctant to agree, but Tosia would not have it any other way. "You must," she said firmly, "and then, little by little, your fame will spread. You will be the greatest pianist in all Europe."

"Not only in Europe," Ignacy protested.

"Well, then, in all the world," Tosia corrected herself, and laughed as she stooped to kiss his rumpled hair.

But not all their hopes and dreams were to be realized. So often, so very often, this is what happens in life, but this knowledge did not make the pain that came to Ignacy Paderewski easier to bear. After a year of life together Tosia died. Ignacy was stunned by the blow. He was alone, entirely alone. The son that Tosia had borne shortly before her death gave him no joy. The warm comfort that his father and all his friends tried to give him did nothing to lift his despair.

He spoke to no one. He saw no one. Day after day he shut himself in his studio with his piano, and played. It was new, sad music that he drew from the instrument now. It had no joy. No gaiety. Just sadness and despair and loneliness.

For a few years Ignacy Paderewski lived alone with his sorrow. His piano was his only companion. With it he conversed, and from it he drew the melody and refrain of the pain that burned in him.

Not until the year 1884 did he succeed in rousing himself from his sorrow, and then it was the recollection of the words that Tosia had spoken to him that helped him. "If I should die," she had said, not once but many times, "then you must take the money we have saved, and continue your studies. Do not let anyone or anything hinder you. A bright future beckons you. I shall hear your music in my grave. I shall live in your melodies."

He had listened to her words with a smile on his lips. She was not going to die, not now, when she was young and joyous and full of life. Nevertheless, he had promised to do as she wished, and now four years after her death, he prepared to keep that promise.

He went to Berlin, and enrolled for the study of composition under Professor Kiel. He worked with great and steady diligence. Often, for many successive days, he sat at the piano for twelve hours, drilling and playing.

Ignacy Paderewski found himself among sincere friends in Berlin. He was known by reputation already, and many homes were opened to receive him. One was that of Hugo Bock, president of the music publishing house of Bote and Bock. While Paderewski was in Berlin, this firm published an album of his short compositions entitled, "Chants du Voyageur."

The young Polish musician met many artists at the home

of Hugo Bock. Richard Strauss, for instance, was a visitor at the Bock home and so were the violinists, Joseph Joachim and Pablo de Sarasate. These famous musicians became his close friends, and it was a source of much pleasure to them to see the twenty-four year old Ignacy developing gradually into a mature pianist. Their friendship buoyed him up greatly. When he became sad and his old grief overwhelmed him, they encouraged him to continue his work. And as he worked, he began to realize anew the power that was in him. The fire for music and achievement had only smoldered. It had never gone out, and now it flamed with marvellous intensity and steadiness.

"I shall be grateful to Tosia forever and ever," he whispered to himself often. "It was she, and she alone, who made me come here. She saved the money. She gave me the very will to come. Her words, 'I shall hear you in my grave,' brought me here."

Although this may not have been entirely true, for it was the music that was in his mind and heart that had surely roused him from his sorrow, yet these precious memories led him on to greater and still greater diligence. He was going to be the world's greatest pianist. Because of his father. Because of Tosia. Ah, yes, and because of the music that was in him.

"If only she could be here! Perhaps, behind those soft clouds, her spirit is hearing my music," he would murmur often.

One day, when these thoughts were leading him back along memory's highway to his life with his young Tosia, he was interrupted by his servant.

"Hurry! Hurry, Herr Paderewski," the old woman cried. "If you do not hurry, you will surely miss the train to Warszawa."

Of course! Of course! His year was up. He was going back to his native land.

He was leaving Berlin with its bleak, cold walls that always seemed to have the oppressive smell of beer emanating from them. Paderewski never liked the taste of beer while he was studying in Berlin, but this dislike did not prevent him from loving the German master musicians who loved their beer.

So now he was returning to his dear Poland. He would rest there. He would talk to his friends. He would practice. He might even begin to teach his little son, Alfred, to pick out simple melodies on the piano. With a soft chuckle, he promised himself many long and tall drinks of rich buttermilk. It would take away the unpleasant recollection of German beer.

Six

From Zakopane the Road Led to Vienna

Helena Modrzejewska, the noted Polish actress whose friendship Ignacy Paderewski achieved when he was a student at the conservatory in Warszawa, returned to her native land from a triumphal tour in America in the summer of 1887. She was a Shakespearian actress of superb quality, certainly one of the most versatile of her time, and her acclaim in America was quite in keeping with that given her in the capitals of Europe. When she returned to Poland, she went at once to her luxurious villa in the Kakopane district, and Ignacy Paderewski went there to be her guest.

From the windows of the villa, the world around was like a fairy tale picture. The Carpathians rolled and billowed and stretched slender peaks to the heavens. The proud Giewont blended his lofty summit with the sky's brilliant blue, and in the golden light of the morning's sun the old gray peaks of Gerlach and Lomnica looked as graceful as young girls. The air was clear and fragrant with the perfume of crocuses and pines. A poet has said that here in the Tatry, as this part of the Carpathians is called, youth is born, and youth renewed.

This was the right environment for Ignacy, tired from his year of constant study and reluctant still to mingle with too many bustling and talkative people. It had been to the Tatry that Tosia had said they would go for their holiday. Now, alas, after five years, he came alone.

The little town that nestled in a shallow valley of the mountains was hidden by trees and towering snow-capped hills, and Madam Modrzejewska's villa was, of all the community of houses, perhaps the most sequestered. Here, Ignacy found two precious things—the comfort of solitude and the pleasure of congenial society. It was no wonder that he composed and played in the silvery dawn and all through the clear, golden hours of the day, and that his compositions were drawn from the customs of the mountain people. His "Tatry Album" is the music of the buoyant air, minarets of mountain snow, and the dances of simple people.

His sojourn in this hospitable home brought him rest and an uninterrupted period for composition. And something else besides—the stimulating companionship of a gracious woman who, from his boyhood, had had unfailing confidence in his gifts.

Helena Modrzejewska was an artist of long and wide experience; she had many friends in various parts of the world, and this summer she invited many of them to her villa for a

63

holiday to meet Ignacy Paderewski. With their assistance, she arranged concerts for him, and at one of them he earned four hundred guldens. Thus, his holiday brought him what he most sorely needed—money to go to Vienna and take lessons from the famous piano teacher, Leschetizky, whom he had met years before in Warszawa.

One of the concerts which Ignacy gave under the sponsorship of Madam Modrzejewska was in the renowned and ancient city of Krakow, and it was before this critical and experienced audience that he first played his "Tatry Album." It is easy to imagine the eagerness that almost suffocated him while he waited for the reception. Would the people applaud? Or would they receive it in dignified, but scornful, silence? Perhaps there would be murmurs of disdain. But, no. The newest composition of the gifted musician was received with wild acclaim. His heart swelled with happiness and pride, for it was an achievement to please the music-loving people of the city that had once been Poland's capital.

And so now to Vienna and Leschetizky. When the time came for his departure, Ignacy may have had a few misgivings, for he had heard many stories of how the great master had listened to would-be students, then shaken his head regretfully, and said, "I cannot give you lessons." Perhaps, the young Pole thought, he would receive as chilly a reception.

Madam Modrzejewska had no such doubts. She had confidence, and gave it to him when she whispered her farewell.

"Go to Vienna," she said. "Learn how Leschetizky brings the voices of angels from his piano. Learn to play as he does, and better. You will surprise the world, and your fame will be good for our enslaved country. For Poland, then, my dear friend."

At that time one man, a fat, untidy man with a gruff voice and an uncouth manner, dominated the music scene of Vienna. He was Johannes Brahms, and shortly after his arrival in the city, Leschetizky and his wife, a well-known pianist, introduced Ignacy Paderewski to the "genius" Brahms. It was a great event in the life of the young Pole, and when he was bowing to him, he was recalling how the word "genius" had at first become attached to Brahms.

It had happened in this way: after Robert Schumann had heard him play for the first time, he had written an article for a magazine in Leipzig, beginning with these enthusiastic words, "Gentlemen! Hats off! A Genius!" From the day of that article's publication, the words "Brahms" and "genius" were always closely associated.

In the first instant of their meeting, Paderewski took a liking to Brahms. He saw him treat his host and hostess with scant courtesy. He saw him eat food greedily, and ignore his table companions entirely; yet, Paderewski knew that beneath Brahms' surliness and bad manners there was a kind and generous heart. He was not just a fat man with short legs, who had a gift for music composition. He was capable of sincere friendship, and Ignacy set himself to win that friendship. Evening after evening in Paderewski's apartment at forty-six Anastasius Grün-Grasse, the two musicians played their compositions for each other. For the first time in his life, Johannes Brahms appeared to care for a human being.

After listening to many of the young musician's compositions, Brahms told Paderewski that he was convinced that he would never become a great original composer. An interpreter of infinite skill, insight, and feeling, yes, but not a composer. The opinion was a hard blow to Paderewski, for he wanted, above all else, to pour his gift of music out in composition. Cruel though the criticism was, Paderewski understood its sincerity. He listened with respect to the assurance that Brahms gave him that he would be a great pianist, probably, indeed, almost certainly, the world's greatest.

It was, in fact, because of Brahms' encouragement that Paderewski arranged his first concert in Vienna. Johannes Brahms and Leschetizky sat in the front row, and applauded enthusiastically.

The first concert in Vienna was so successful that it was followed by many others. Agents and critics came from Paris and Berlin to hear them, with the result that long before his period of study in Vienna was over, Ignacy Paderewski had invitations to give concerts in both the capitals of France and Germany.

All his life, Paderewski said that his real career in concert playing began because his two devoted friends, Brahms and Leschetizky, encouraged and guided him. From Vienna, the gay and beautiful city on the Danube, the fame of the Polish pianist rose like a rising tide.

At one of his most successful concerts in Vienna, Paderewski paid his teacher a lovely tribute. When autograph seekers asked him to sign their concert programmes, he wrote, "Theodor Leschetizky's grateful pupil, I. J. Paderewski."

Seven

The Lion of Paris

Throughout his life, Ignacy Paderewski had a gift for winning and holding friends. He was loyal in his friendships and a similar loyalty was bestowed on him. Partly through the encouragement and the material assistance of his friends, he was able to go to Paris to give concerts when he was not quite twenty-eight years old.

While he was in Berlin and Vienna, Paderewski had been separated from his little son, Alfred, but now he brought him to Paris to live with him in the two-roomed studio he had taken at number ninety-four Victor Hugo Avenue. Paderewski had a deep affection for his son, who was now nearly eight years old, but sorrow mingled with his devotion, for Alfred was a cripple. He could not walk, and was seldom free of pain. With increasing diligence that was almost desperation.

the father searched Paris for a doctor who could find some clue to the strange illness that would not leave the child. Sometimes he himself took the child to doctors who were recommended; sometimes Alfred was taken by the motherly Madam Gorski, whose husband was a violinist and a friend of Paderewski's. But no doctor could discover the cause of the illness that was like prison chains on the little boy, nor prescribe a cure for the sickness that slowly progressed in intensity. To-day, doctors would probably recognize the ailment as infantile paralysis.

There were occasions during his life in Paris that Ignacy Paderewski played the piano for hours at a time, for no other reason than to shut out the memory of his son's suffering. He was such a little boy to have to bear so great a burden. Another ever-present sorrow was the loss of his wife. He needed her now, and so did Alfred. The keys of the piano, responding so willingly to his command, alone brought him relief and happiness. And so he played—played constantly—and with deep, very deep feeling.

The fame of Paderewski spread rapidly while he was in Paris. London heard of him not only through the correspondents of the various newspapers who reported his concerts, but by word of mouth from travellers returning to England from France. In the same way New York heard of him. French artists welcomed him to their exclusive society, and French aristocrats, finding that his social graces were exceedingly agreeable, opened their homes to him.

Charles Francis Gounod, then in the twilight of his long life, became his friend and to some extent, his mentor. Gounod had lived in England during the Franco-Prussian war, and from this experience, he was able to give the young musician much advice on what to do in order to break through what most continental people considered the chilly indifference of the English. The great Sarah Bernhardt, returned recently from her first triumphal visit to America, became his friend, too, and in vivacious anecdotes and by serious descriptions portrayed American audiences to him. There were others of the theater and concert stage who extended cordial welcome to Paderewski while he was in Paris. In fact a catalogue of his associates in Paris would be long and varied and probably tedious, but the names of Camille Saint-Saëns, Jules Massenet, and Frederic Mistral, the poet, should be mentioned.

The night of Paderewski's first concert in Paris arrived. It was to be given in the Salle Erard, and he was to play the thirty-two "Variations in C Minor" by Beethoven and the "Sixth Rhapsody" by Liszt. Long before the concert began, the attendants brought word to his dressing-room that the most illustrious artists of all Paris were arriving. One attendant whispered that in his opinion people had come from London and Rome and Vienna for the express purpose of attending his concert. Madam Dubois, the last person to study under Chopin, was there. So was Auguste Rodin, whose statues always called forth stormy debates and as enthusiastic praise. And Tschaikovsky, the Russian composer, was there. This knowledge must have fired Paderewski with a flaming resolution to do even better than his best, for Tschaikovsky was at the very height of his fame. Moreover, as he was a Russian, he might be inclined to look askance at a Polish musician, and Ignacy

Paderewski was determined to show him that a Polish artist could far surpass a Russian.

Paderewski excelled himself, as he had prayed that he would do, and even while he was making his final bows to an applauding audience, the Russian composer was leaving his seat and making his way to the back of the stage. Tschaikovsky shook the young Pole's hand many times, and quite frankly said that he was astonished by his gift. Was it because he was Polish that he was so surprised, Paderewski wondered haughtily, and then wisely decided not to ask the question.

It was always hard for him to forget that his country, Poland, was under the heel of the czar of all the Russias, and in the first moments of his meeting with Tschaikovsky a torrent of recollections swept through his mind: the day when the Cossacks had come to arrest his father; his first visit to the Ukrainian city of Kiev when he had seen dreadful poverty and sumptuous display of riches; the misery of the peasants of Sudylkow; and many, many more unhappy memories. However, the introductory greetings were the most difficult, and soon the two were talking cordially. They dined together that night and drank champagne which, next to milk, was Paderewski's favorite drink.

When the night was nearly gone, the two men, rapidly becoming friends, went out to walk along the Seine and watch the dawn spread its cold light over the city. As they walked, they talked of their countries. Tschaikovsky in his early youth had worked as a clerk in the czar's Ministry of Justice, and had a high esteem for the governmental system of Russia. When Paderewski said accusingly that Russia was torturing Poland, ruining her culture, and suffocating the spirit of her people, Tschaikovsky rose at once to the defense of his country's government in Poland.

"The czar of Russia is a wise man. He has the best interests of all the people he rules close to his heart," Tschaikovsky proclaimed in resonant tones.

"Is sending thousands to Siberia and sentencing as many to the gallows having his people close to his heart?" Paderewski asked disdainfully.

Before his companion could say anything he continued, "Your czar is persecuting my people. He has made slaves of us."

"Slaves!" and Tschaikovsky's scorn was even more vehement than Paderewski's. "Slaves!" he cried. "Why Russia has freed the Polish peasants. They no longer live in feudal bondage. They may own land. They are free men now."

"Not until they rose in revolt did he free them," Paderewski shouted, and hurled a question at Tschaikovsky. "Do you know what kind of land your czar gave them? Starved, hungry land, that is what it is."

It was Tschaikovsky's turn now and he demanded, "Who starved it but the Polish noblemen? Not the czar of Russia. And who held it greedily and would not give it up? Polish noblemen, of course, and they would have it yet, if our wise and generous ruler had not intervened. I tell you, the czar has released the downtrodden Polish peasants from slavery imposed on them by Polish noblemen." As he said this like someone delivering a proclamation, he shook his bearded chin in Paderewski's face.

"I have nothing to say in defense of Polish noblemen," Paderewski answered, "for they were the cause of Poland's downfall, but do not tell me, Peter Tschaikovsky, that the czar of Russia is the benefactor of my people. I know better. He is cruel and—."

There was a splash. A smothered scream. Another scream. Poland, the czar, noblemen, and the starved condition of Polish soil, were forgotten for a moment. Tschaikovsky was the first to see someone struggling in the Seine waters.

"See! A man!" he cried.

In a second Paderewski had his coat off, and dived into the muddy river. He was gone for fifteen minutes, fifteen very long minutes. Tschaikovsky had a carriage waiting for him when he came ashore, dragging an unconscious woman with him. They wasted no time in words, but bundled her into the carriage and hurried off to Paderewski's apartment. After they had revived her with brandy and hot tea and she had wrapped herself in a woolen blanket, she told them her unhappy story.

"I come from Poland," she said brokenly. "I have been in Paris six months. My husband and nineteen-year-old son died in prison in Warszawa."

She paused to stifle her sobs and the two men waited.

"The czar's policemen tried to arrest me, as they had my husband and son," she said, "but on the night they came for me, I escaped through a window. It took me a long time to get here. Weeks and months." The woman sobbed.

There was another long pause. Paderewski filled her cup again, but neither he nor Tschaikovsky pressed her with questions.

"I thought I would find friends here. There are so many Polish people in Paris," she said at last. "I thought I would find work, too. But, no, I could not. I had no food and no family. There seemed no place for me but the merciful Seine."

"Who was your husband?" Paderewski asked softly.

"He was a teacher in a gymnasium in Warszawa," she answered, "and his only crime was that he taught his students the true story of our country's servitude to the czar. He organized them into a body to fight for Poland's freedom."

Paderewski patted her hand. He understood the bitter consequences of being a patriot in Poland. All his life, he had seen people being sent to Siberia, and returning from Siberia.

"My son and I were accused by the czarist police of working in a secret revolutionary organization," she said. A torrent of sobs shook her.

As she became quiet again, the slender, pale fingers of the dawn stole into the room. The candles, burned low now, sputtered and went out. A new day had come and as the woman saw it, a flicker of a smile crept over her white face. Dawn brings hope, even to the most desolate.

Paderewski looked at Tschaikovsky and wondered anxiously if the story of this woman's pain might have won his country some sympathy. If it had, then a new dawn might begin to rise on a distant, far distant, horizon for Poland, for Tschaikovsky was an esteemed friend of the czar's. It was a feeble hope that stirred in Paderewski's heart, one in which his mind had no great confidence.

Tschaikovsky now rose from the chair where he had sat, silent and with bowed head, while the woman had been talking,

73

and went over to her. He took her trembling hand in his and kissed it. Then he shook Paderewski's hand humbly, even apologetically, and went out without saying a word.

From that time on, Tschaikovsky, the composer and the devoted friend of the czar, became an ardent supporter of Poland's struggle for freedom. He studied her history and the laws that czarist imperialism had put upon her. He saw and felt the cruelty of her condition, and with the passing years, sorrow and melancholy crept into his music. The grief of an unfortunate woman was in many of his melodies, and the cause of an unfortunate country was often in his mind.

Eight

By Royal Command

A thin, gray mist of fog and smoke hung like a cloud over London. Only occasionally, the sun broke through to give a little warmth to the chilly day. At an early hour a man came out of a grim-faced building in the neighborhood of Russell Square, and entered a closed carriage. There is no record that says how many horses were hitched to the vehicle, but probably there were four prancing steeds and probably there were two coachmen, dressed in royal livery sitting on the box. The horses' hoofs clicked smartly on the cobbled road and the coach rolled off on its twenty-mile journey.

The passenger in the carriage was Ignacy Paderewski. By royal command, he was going to Windsor Castle. Her Majesty, the Queen of Great Britain and Ireland and of the Dominions beyond the Seas, and Empress of India, had summoned him to play before her and the members of the royal household.

The journey to Windsor took a long time. The ancient road led over hills and through valleys and past many little "pubs" and post-houses, with the blue ribbon of the Thames nearly always in sight. As he was driven swiftly through the country-side, a multitude of thoughts filled Paderewski's mind. He thought of the old woman at Windsor who had commanded him to appear before her. She was a tiny woman with kind blue eyes and an imperious manner. Her laughter was deep and rich and her speech was dignified and slightly German in its quality. This much he knew and more, too, for since the command had been received, Daniel Mayer, his agent, had given him many vivid descriptions of the "widow at Windsor," a name given to Queen Victoria shortly after the death of her consort and it had stayed with her through the years.

"She is very fond of music," Daniel Mayer had said, "and is no mean musician herself. Mendelssohn, you know, came from Germany to teach her."

Paderewski recalled this now as his carriage rattled up to the lofty eminence, on which Windsor Castle stands, and as the horses sped along the drive to the entrance of the private resi-dence, another thought came to his mind. It was of Britain's support of his country, Poland. Britain had protested to Russia on one occasion, at least, because of that country's high-handed treatment of the Polish people. Many people believed, so Daniel Mayer had told Paderewski, that the protest had been inspired by Queen Victoria.

"She knows the tragedy of my country," the young musician said to himself, "and in her warm heart she sympathizes with us." The thought gave him confidence as he waited for the great doors to swing open.

A liveried footman led him to the long, gracious music-room, where he was received by the queen's youngest daughter, Princess Beatrice, and soon the queen herself arrived, looking very tiny and very old and not at all like a royal personage. She had been ill and was wheeled into the room in an invalid's chair. For a time she and the musician talked of music and she asked him questions about his country—its art, its history, and especially, about its country people. He was thrilled to find her so full of knowledge of Poland and her social and economic problems.

When at last he was seated at the piano, he drew golden music from the magnificent instrument. He played selections of his own choosing, and it was the clear ecstatic melodies of Chopin that rolled into the great room, and held the royal mistress of Windsor spellbound. The music reverberated through the whole palace. The cooks in the kitchen heard it and stopped their work to listen. The attendants in the gallery left their posts and moved nearer to the doors of the music-room. The music sounded out into the gardens, and even found its way to the ears of the guards in the main part of the castle. The great trees in the Windsor garden must have heard the full sweeping melodies of the Wisla and of the Polish fields and forests, and bowed their heads in greeting to this salutation from a distant land.

This was Ignacy Paderewski's first appearance before the British ruler, but in the future he was to receive many royal commands and to become the friend of several members of the royal family. His heart was filled with joy and sadness as he took his leave of the queen and her daughters, Princess Louise and Princess Beatrice. The joy came from the knowledge that he had played well for a little old woman who loved music. The sorrow was something that was with him constantly. If only he were returning to his hotel in London to tell Tosia of his success, Tosia who had said that he must conquer Europe!

And he had conquered Europe, even stern, reserved Britain. It had not been easy, this winning of British acclaim, for the English people seldom showed much enthusiasm for an artist given magnificent ovations in Paris. The British, so it was said in the closing years of the last century, had no wish to be guided by the French in their selection of artists. Paris had been wildly enthusiastic about Paderewski. It was natural, then, for the British to be a little dubious of him.

It was unfortunate that Daniel Mayer should have shown so little understanding of the British temperament as to put Paderewski before them as "Lion of Paris." However, it did not take the musician long to erase his unfavorable introduction. He became the great success of the London season of 1890 and 1891. Long before he was summoned to the queen's presence, he had given concerts in all the big cities of Great Britain, with the exception of Glasgow, and the biggest event of many seasons was his concert in St. James's Hall, London.

The doors of England's most stately homes were opened to him, and he became friends with many of Britain's leading artists, among them two painters, Burne-Jones and Alma-Tadema. One friendship which he formed in London at this time lasted for nearly half a century. It was with Lady Barrington, whose husband, Sir Eric Barrington, was the secretary of Lord Salisbury, then Prime Minister. This was a cordial and happy friendship that ended only with the death of Lady Barrington in 1937.

Only one music critic in London failed to acclaim Paderewski after his first concerts in Great Britain. He was a tall, gaunt, red-haired fellow who had a sharp wit and a trenchant pen. He was the critic of "The World" and his name was Bernard Shaw. There were many reasons for the "doubting Thomas" attitude of Shaw. One may have been that he was under the influence of the German critics, none of whom had shown any appreciation of Paderewski who had begun his concert career not in Berlin but in Vienna, and had gone from there to Paris. Another reason, and a more likely one, for Mr. Shaw's attitude to Paderewski may have been his unwillingness to acclaim any artist who so obviously strove to win the favor of the aristocracy. Bernard Shaw was an ardent and sincere socialist and he probably believed that artists should not need the sponsorship of rich lords and ladies.

On the night of his return from Windsor Castle, Paderewski went out to walk in the narrow streets of London. Even though the fog had grown thick and hung close about him like a cloak, he found his way to the Embankment, and sat for a time in the shadow of Cleopatra's Needle, watching the dim passage of the boats on the Thames and listening to their hoarse fog-horns mingling from time to time with the thunderous peel of "Big Ben." He was happy, so very happy, for he knew that he had won a friend at Windsor, and that in the achievement he had renewed the queen's interest in his country's struggle for freedom. But he was sad, too, on this night, for he had no one with whom to share his happiness. Tosia was dead, and his father, bowed now with years and living in the darkness of almost complete blindness, was far away in Poland.

As he sat there, the shadows and noises of London all about him, his mind went back over the years of his life. He recalled the happy days of his life with Tosia; then the days of his childhood when his sister Antonina had been his companion; then back again to sweet memories of Tosia. As he sat in the gloom, he could, in imagination, hear her whispering her pleasure in him and in his success. Then many sounds from the storehouse of his memory came ringing in his ears. He heard the harvesters singing in the harvest fields; he heard the children playing in the muddy streets of Sudylkow; he heard Siwek neighing and calling to him imperiously to roam country lanes and forest trails with him; he heard wolves howling on the road from Kiev and the flames crackling through a burning sleigh.

But memories are only for the old and the idle, not for young men who have much to achieve and much to give to the world. He shook himself free of them and began to walk again, this time toward Soho and his favorite Italian restaurant.

Fat Papa Bellini was waiting for him and helped him off with his coat and muffler. "I was expecting you, Mr. Paderewski," he said, "for I read in the paper that you were returning from Windsor to-day, and your friends, too, are waiting for you."

He pointed toward a table near the hearth, and Paderewski saw that Daniel Mayer and a group of his friends were sitting there. Mayer rose and hurried to him.

"At last! At last!" he exclaimed. "We had almost given you up, but not quite, for we thought you would keep your promise to come here to tell us of your reception at Windsor."

A sudden smile came to Paderewski's face and its happiness chased the sadness from his countenance.

"You see," one friend cried, "he had forgotten about us, and about Windsor, too, I'll warrant. I could tell it by his expression when Bellini greeted him. He has been living Poland's tribulations again, and thinking of his native village."

"True! True!" Paderewski laughed, "but now, my friends, I am ready to laugh with you."

"It's always the same," Daniel Mayer said. "He returns with a sorrowful countenance from a successful concert. Always!"

They laughed and lifted their wine glasses in a toast. When it was drunk, Mr. Mayer took a long envelope from his pocket.

"You have been invited to America for a concert tour," he said.

There were exclamations and congratulations. Would he accept the invitation? When would he go? For how long? Would he return to London afterwards? Paderewski could not begin to answer the questions, for once more memories claimed him. They were happy memories this time, for they were of a young boy called Ignacy Paderewski, sitting at a piano in his aunt's drawing-room, and looking out on a sunny, flower-decked meadow in Poland. The boy was dreaming dreams of his future, and at the same time music was surging like a swiftly moving stream through his mind.

Nine

First American Successes

On a very bleak day in early November of the year 1891, the good ship *Spray* docked in the harbor of New York. She had had a stormy passage from England: the wind had blown a gale, and even as she came alongside, she was still creaking in her timbers and her passengers were still shuddering in their great coats and mufflers. The harbor aspect of New York had nothing of comfort to offer the storm-tossed voyagers, for it was shrouded in fog and a biting wind was the only greeting extended to them as they stood in huddled groups, waiting for the gang-plank to be lowered.

Two men stood by themselves at the rail, and peered down at the upturned faces of the few people gathered to meet the ship. There was not a familiar face among them—the two new arrivals looked at each other forlornly. They were lonely, filled with misgiving, almost frightened, yet each tried to smile encouragement to the other and each strove to form a few words of encouragement for the other. After all, in Europe everyone spoke of America as a land of golden opportunity, a wonderful land where dreams come true. As a matter of fact, they had had material evidence of this before they left London, for one of them had been guaranteed thirty thousand American dollars.

One of the men was Ignacy Jan Paderewski. The other one was his secretary, Hugo Goerlitz.

"Six million Poles in this country," Paderewski murmured with a rueful smile, "and yet not one of them has come to welcome us."

His heart was heavy. It was as if the cold Atlantic winds had pierced it and laid a stone of bitterness and desolation on it. He remembered his first lonely days in Warszawa, when he had longed so for his father and his sister Antonina. He recalled his tour in Russia and the days when he had tossed with fever in St. Petersburg. Surely loneliness would not engulf him completely in America.

After all, was someone seeking them out, coming toward them with hand outstretched? Yes, the smile was for them. The man was Mr. Tretbach and he had come from Steinway & Sons to welcome Mr. Paderewski. The first sickening sense of loneliness vanished, but it was to return in a few hours, when the two newcomers discovered that the hotel accommodation provided for them was far from pleasant. The hotel was in the vicinity of Union Square and they had no quarrel with the location. It was the immediate environment that caused the musician to enquire protestingly in broken English, "If one is eaten alive and nothing but his bones are left, then who will play?"

A few hours after the protest, Mr. Paderewski and Mr. Goerlitz were in congenial surroundings in the Windsor Hotel on Fifth Avenue at Forty-Sixth Street. From that gracious building Mr. Paderewski went, on the night of November the seventeenth, to give his first concert in America at Carnegie Hall. The orchestra was conducted by Mr. Walter Damrosch who began the concert with Golmark's overture entitled, "In Spring-time." The Polish master played compositions of Saint-Saëns, Chopin, and his own Concerto No. 1, Opus 17.

At first the audience was attentive and curiosity mingled with its interest. The press reports from Paris had been extravagant; those from London, though restrained and dignified, had suggested a talent of amazing magnitude. Well, America was ready to be shown. Interest grew to pleasure, pleasure to delight, and the applause rang to the roof of the hall. Ignacy Paderewski had once more conquered a great audience and an impressive group of critics. After many encores the people rose from their seats to depart, but many stayed to talk of the most recent arrival from Europe. They were impressed with his hands; his fingers were like fairies dancing on the keys. The intensity of his feeling, as he drew deep, rich melodies from the piano, was like the outpouring of a being of superhuman power. They realized that Paderewski lived the music he played.

"It is natural that Poland should have artists whose hearts are on fire," one man said. "Artistic genius so often burns with unquenchable fire, when a nation is suffering under foreign domination."

The man's companion laughed grimly and answered, "True, and when one listens to Paderewski or to Helena Modrzejewska or the brothers Reszke the price does not seem too high."

After three concerts in New York City Paderewski went on what proved to be a tour of triumph to Boston, Philadelphia, Chicago, Los Angeles, and Milwaukee. Audiences in several smaller cities were privileged to hear him, too: among them, Santa José on the west coast; St. Joseph, Missouri; Springfield, Massachusetts; and Portland, Maine.

In Boston more than in any other city in America, Mr. Paderewski felt at home. He liked its old world quality. The narrow, crooked streets and the stern-faced buildings, the clatter of cargoes being landed and others being loaded, the pervading smell of fish, the more than misty fogs, the leisurely progress of traffic—all these reminded him of certain continental cities where he had lived and been among friends. He spent a great deal of time in the Tavern Club of Boston and also in pleasant association with the Polish-American family by the name of Adamowski. His diary had other names in it, too, especially that of Joshua Montgomery Sears.

Back in New York once more, this affable artist found himself quite as much of a lion as he had been in Paris, where his fair hair first won him the name, "Lion of Paris." The doors of many homes were opened to him, and he found congenial friends within—people who loved him not only for his music, but because of his good manners and his kindly ways. There was another reason, too: the fire of patriotism burned high in him; love of country gave him and many Americans a common ground. His diary of the time had the names of Chase, Vanderbilt, Gilder, and Carnegie in it frequently.

The Gilder home was a rendezvous for many artists. Mr. Gilder was the editor of Century Magazine and he and Ignacy Paderewski became warm friends. It was at the Gilder's home that he met Mark Twain, with whom he struck up a friendship that lasted as long as the humorist lived. On many cold nights the three, pianist, author, and editor, sat before the glowing hearth in Mr. Gilder's study on Eighth Street, and discussed art and, more particularly, the course of art in a new country like America. They talked of European politics, too, and the way in which American trends were sometimes reflected in the political and economic reforms in European countries. After these talks Mark Twain and Ignacy Paderewski would take long walks in the crisp, clear night. They both enjoyed the snow that glittered in the pale moonlight, and as they walked, they talked more about the new world that both were confident was growing, a world where music and literature and art would be within the grasp of all who wanted them. What dreams these two, one a pianist of world repute and the other a humorist of equal fame, wove so brilliantly as they crunched the snow under their feet!

It was Paderewski's custom when he was in New York to go to the Steinway Piano Warehouse on Fourteenth Street to practise. He would sit by the hour playing Nocturne—Prelude —Etude—Ballad. On one particular day, he finished at five o'clock, and then went to the Gilders' for tea. Mrs. Gilder received him with a laughing exclamation of, "Oh, Mr. Paderewski, you're just the person we need at this instant. Francesca wants to dance and she wants someone to play for her."

"Good! I'll play for your young daughter," Mr. Paderewski said, and sat down at the piano.

A moving picture of village children dancing on a village green in Poland drifted before his mind's eye. Then he saw boys and girls, barefoot and ragged, laughing and singing and dancing at a festival. The dream grew until Francesca was forgotten, and in her place were the Ukrainian, Jewish, and Polish friends of his childhood. He played as he might have played for them.

Francesca was forgotten, but not for very long! She had started to waltz, but could not keep in time. Mr. Paderewski changed the tune, but alas, again there was trouble. Francesca stood perfectly still, her piquant little face puckered with anger.

"Mr. Paderewski doesn't know how to play," she stormed wrathfully. "My governess can play much better and I can dance to her music."

In a flash Francesca was running up the stairs, sobbing with indignation as she went. Her mother called to her to return, but Francesca had lost her wish to dance. In that moment she was far from impressed with the music of Ignacy Paderewski.

"All America is applauding your music," Mrs. Gilder said to Mr. Paderewski, "but not my Francesca. She alone has announced a decided aversion to it."

"Francesca and I, just we two," Mr. Paderewski said. "We have this in common—neither of us likes the music of Paderewski. Ah, well, perhaps some day we shall overcome our dislike."

There was truth in what he said, for Ignacy Paderewski was never satisfied with his music. It tantalized him; it irritated him; he wanted it to be better, more interpretive of the inspiration that had given it birth. He wanted it to be fuller and deeper, to have the strength of the world surging through it.

Perhaps Francesca Gilder grew to love the music of Ignacy Paderewski, but the artist himself never did. It never satisfied him; always he was striving to make it better, to put more feeling and greater skill into it, to draw more golden tones from the piano he played.

Ten

The Blind Negro

The philanthropic works of Andrew Carnegie, who began life in a poor cottage in Dunfermline in Scotland, are known throughout the world. There is no need to enumerate them here—libraries, universities, organizations founded to try to achieve world peace—all these and many more owed their development to Mr. Carnegie. What is important to the story of Ignacy Paderewski is that Andrew Carnegie loved music. He loved the shrill, weird music of the bagpipes and when he had guests at his Skibo Castle, he had them summoned to dinner by the call of the pipes. He loved the majestic music of the organ, and usually his guests had dinner to the music of Bach played by a well-known organist on the giant organ of Skibo Castle. But the music he loved most was that of the piano. With the soft music of the piano sounding in his ears, he could forget the problems of industry that were so constantly before him.

Shortly after his arrival in America, Ignacy Paderewski met Andrew Carnegie and the two, one so affable in manner and the other reserved almost to the point of being dour, became friends. Music, without doubt, was what first brought them together, but later, they found another interest. Paderewski's intense patriotism and his resolute purpose to do all in his power to release his country from its Russian bondage kindled a spark in Carnegie, who had fought a bitter and amazingly successful battle against poverty.

A few years before their meeting, Carnegie's book, *Triumphant Democracy*, had been published and he was then engaged in writing *The Gospel of Wealth*. The conditions of a changing world must have engrossed them on many evenings and Carnegie probably smiled reminiscently many times at the theories propounded by the young musician from Poland. He had the same enthusiasm and the same resolution that a lad from Dunfermline had had so many years before. He remembered that lad well, Andrew Carnegie did, for the wealth and power he achieved never erased the memory of the hunger and hard work of his youth.

Ignacy Paderewski visited Andrew Carnegie at his home on Fifth Avenue in New York City and at his summer home in Massachusetts, and when he played the piano for Mr. Carnegie and his guests, he usually chose the music of Chopin. There was something indescribably fascinating in Chopin's dance rhythms and in the long slender fingers of Paderewski drawing the strange poetic imagery from the piano. Carnegie and his guests were held spellbound by the magnificent flow of music, and the musician himself, when he paused in his playing to consider his audience, must have been eager to give his listeners the very best that was in him.

They were illustrious people whom Andrew Carnegie invited to listen to him. William McKinley was seated in a much-carved chair, placed beneath an elaborate painting of Bible times. Joseph Pulitzer watched the swift fingers of the pianist, and smiled with pleasure. Miss Eleanor Blodgett of the family of Lorin Blodgett sat near the fireplace, and beside her a vigorous old man with keen eyes and a resolute mouth— Joseph Choate—soon to be elected president of the New York State Constitutional Convention, and after that to be ambassador to Great Britain. Theodore Thomas, the conductor, sat near the piano, his eyes held by the grace and power of Paderewski's fingers. And there were others in the gathering, so a newspaper of the time, probably Mr. Pulitzer's "World," recorded: Miss Etta Dunham, Miss Arnold, and Mrs. William H. Draper.

One night after one of these feasts of music at Mr. Carnegie's home, Ignacy Paderewski retired to his room to write some music. All evening as he played and talked, the melody had been whirling around in his head and he was anxious to set it down. Before beginning his work, he asked Joe, Mr. Carnegie's old negro servant, to bring him a pot of black coffee. Ignacy Paderewski always wrote music with a cup of black coffee near at hand.

Joe had had a long, tiresome day. His feet were like lead on this night and his smile was not as broad and happy as it usually was. Nevertheless, he trotted off willingly to do Mr. Paderewski's bidding, and perhaps as he went he was thinking to himself that he liked to serve this golden-haired man from a faraway country. And perhaps, he was thinking, as his tired calloused feet carried him down the staircase, that he was growing too old for the "run and carry" life of a house-servant. Yes, that probably was the thought that hovered in his mind, for Joe had been a servant in Andrew Carnegie's home for forty-five years.

But whatever the thoughts of the old man may have been, they were put to flight by a sudden stumble and a quick crash. He had missed the top step of the staircase and had fallen. The hot coffee poured over his face and into his eyes. He was a crumpled heap when Paderewski came rushing to his rescue. His groans were deep and agonized when the pianist lifted him in his arms and carried him to his bed-room. He put him down on his bed, and then ran for help. A doctor came and bandaged Joe's eyes, while Ignacy Paderewski stood by whispering words of encouragement to the sufferer.

When the doctor was leaving, Mr. Paderewski accompanied him to the door. Would the old man soon be better? Yes, soon, but not entirely better. The doctor spoke solemnly and the words he said were, "He may be blind."

Blind! Ignacy Paderewski knew what that meant. From his childhood he had seen his father's sight failing. He knew the helplessness of the near-blind. He knew how they tried to hide their affliction and how desolate they felt when familiar faces gradually faded from their sight. His warm heart ached for the old white-haired negro. After the doctor had gone, Paderewski went back to his room and sat down on a sofa near Joe. He whispered a few words of regret to the old man, and at the same time told him that the doctor had said that he would be around soon.

"Please, Sir, do not blame yourself for the accident," Joe begged. "I am an old man and I should have stopped trying to do a young man's work long ago."

Ignacy Paderewski sat with old Joe for a long time. There is no record of what they said. Perhaps they talked very little, and only in the nearness of the one to the other gave comfort to each other. However, during that night Ignacy Paderewski won a devoted friend and Joe, likewise, achieved a sincere friend.

In a few months the negro was as completely recovered as was possible. One eye was gone and the little sight that remained in the other was just enough to enable him to discern darkness from daylight. But the color of Joe's world was by no means gloomy. Something wonderful had happened to him while he was resting in a darkened room. He had been given a farm in his native Georgia, and he was to return there to live in comfort on his own land, for all the rest of his life. Every day he would be able to hear the laughter and chatter of his grandchildren, and when he wanted to walk through his garden or to the sunny side of his house, their keen eyes and strong hands would be there to guide him. And all his comfort and security had been given to him by Ignacy Paderewski.

Several of Mr. Paderewski's friends protested that he was being altogether too generous with the old negro. It was not his fault that he had missed a step of the staircase, and fallen. The pianist listened to his friends, and usually made no comment, but on one occasion he answered them.

"You recall that a Polish general fought with Washington, don't you?" he asked.

"Yes," one friend answered, "Kosciuszko."

Paderewski nodded and put a second question.

"Then do you remember how he was compensated for his assistance?" he asked.

The friend did. General Kosciuszko had been given a large tract of land by the American Government but, instead of using it himself, he had given it to poor people, and had required no payment from them.

"My countryman of long ago gave me a noble example to follow," Paderewski said, and after that there were no protests nor arguments about his gift to old Joe.

Eleven

Return to Europe

When Ignacy Paderewski gave a concert, there was an old man in the Ukrainian city of Zhitomir waiting eagerly for news of it. He was a very old man who leaned heavily on his cane when he walked. His sight was dim and his voice trembled. His name was Jan Paderewski and he lived in a house that his famous son had bought for him, not far from Sudylkow and the estate where he had worked when Ignacy and Antonina, his two children, were growing up.

Even though his health was not good and his sight was failing, Mr. Jan Paderewski was a happy man. The mail brought him letters from his son regularly, and in between letters there were sheaves of newspaper clippings and packages of concert programmes. They came from Paris and London and New York. They came from lesser cities; some of them he had never heard of before and he found the names hard to say to his friends. Sometimes interesting looking parcels came with the letters, and bore the same little-known postmarks. When a parcel came, Mr. Paderewski would summon his neighbors to see his gift, and frequently he would share it with them. When a box of shortbread came from Edinburgh, for instance, the neighbors enjoyed its crisp richness with Mr. Paderewski. They tasted certain London blends of tea, as well, and probably thought that they were by no means as delicious as their own. They marvelled at the thick pelt of a fox fur robe that came from America, and admired the Indian craftsmanship that made moccasins both warm and beautiful.

Mr. Jan Paderewski kept a scrapbook of newspaper clippings about his son, Ignacy, and the walls of his sitting-room were lined with concert programmes and pictures of him. He would sit by the hour talking of him. He liked to tell of his childhood and of how, when he was no more than three, he could pick out tunes on the piano. He told, too, of his early days at the conservatory in Warszawa, and he would laugh scornfully when he came to the part about Ignacy's rebellion against horned instruments.

"There were those who thought they knew better than he," Mr. Paderewski would say, "but he knew Ignacy always knew, that the piano was his instrument."

When the friends showed their approval of this statement, Mr. Paderewski would continue, pausing only long enough to pass the vodka around or to urge them to have more cookies. He

told them of Ignacy's first journey to Kiev with Count Chodkiewicz and the Baron Horoch and of the splendid day of his
graduation from the conservatory at Warszawa. Then, if the
friends were particularly attentive and had asked him a great
number of interesting questions, he would drop his voice to a
mournful whisper and tell them of Tosia's death. Together,
Jan Paderewski and his visitors would wipe tears from their
eyes, and with no one speaking for awhile, they would all
look at the pictures on the wall or read the most recently
arrived clippings.

From near and far, friends and relatives came to visit Mr.
Jan Paderewski. A cynic might have said that they came to
drink his vodka and eat his food, for both were always plenti-
ful and good, but that was not the primary reason. They
came because they loved to hear the old man tell about his son
and because they wanted to hear of the great world, so far,
far away it seemed to them, that he was discovering. San
José, California—now how many miles was that from Zhitomir? And Queen Victoria—she was an empress, too—what
was she like? A tiny woman in a plain black dress? They
could hardly believe it.

Without doubt, Mr. Paderewski was a happy man and his
son was happy in that knowledge. There were many times
when Ignacy Paderewski must have longed for his home and
his family. His sister, Antonina, the companion of his childhood—he had not seen her for a long time. And his son,
Alfred—was the nurse taking good care of him and were the
doctors trying to find a cure for his sickness? Although he
had confidence in Madam Gorski who looked after the little

boy, he worried about him a great deal, and longed to be with him.

One day Mr. Jan Paderewski had wonderful news. His son was coming home. Even now, while the letter was being read to him, his son was on the ocean bound for Hamburg. In a few days he would be in Zhitomir. Tears of joy filled the old man's eyes. At last! At last! He had waited so long for this day and now it was almost a reality.

The day came and Jan Paderewski and his son, Ignacy, who had travelled half round the world and back, sat together in the little sitting-room of the house in Zhitomir, and talked and talked of the years they had been separated. The father had many questions to ask, especially about America, for like most Polish people he knew many families who had left Poland and gone to seek their fortunes in America. Most of all, of course, the old man wanted to know about his son's concerts. Had the concert halls been crowded? Had the applause in Chicago, for instance, been more vociferous than that in Paris? Oh, there were so many questions, and Ignacy, finally, had to refuse to answer the old man's queries until he took time to give replies to the question that he, Ignacy, wanted answered.

The holiday in Zhitomir could not last long. There were engagements to be filled in France and Germany. And there was something else to do: the year before, 1893, Alfred Nossig, a Polish writer, had suggested to Ignacy Paderewski that he write an opera to be called "Manru." The idea had appealed so much to the pianist that he began work on it at once and now, that he had returned to Europe, he was resolved to complete it. He took it with him to France when he left Zhitomir, and had just started work on it when the news of his father's death came to him. This was not a shock for he had observed the old man's frailness, but he was, nevertheless, overcome with grief. He cancelled his concerts, and could find no heart to continue with the composition of the opera.

The loss of his father was like the breaking up of his world. He felt, for a time, as if music was not his world at all, but that the bond that kept him close to his family was the world for which he worked—and now the integral part of that bond was gone. He remained in almost complete seclusion for nearly two years, and all the time, as he practised and tried to think of nothing but music, he was schooling himself for another sorrow that he felt must come to him. His son was growing steadily worse. The furrows of pain on his brow were growing deeper and his body weaker.

In the year 1898, he was induced to leave his seclusion to play at a few concerts given for the benefit of poor artists in Warszawa. At first he was reticent and even fearful of himself, but soon gentle smiles wreathed his pale face, and then, almost as if unknown to himself, he was laughing with old friends. His old friend and teacher at the conservatory, Professor Roguski, came to greet him and beg him to meet a group of his fellow-countrymen who greatly admired him. Edward Kerntopf, the mentor of his youth, was there, too, and when he saw him a full tide of joy welled up in Paderewski's heart. How he loved his old friends and the ancient city that was his country's capital! He was even able to smile at those old professors who had prophesied very meagre success in music for him. He shook their hands cordially and when they drank a toast to his greater success his heart held no bitterness toward them. Indeed, the memory of their discouraging words was like the recollection of something that had happened so long ago that it might have been in another world and another life.

From the concert and banquet halls of Warszawa, he did not return to his solitary existence, but went to Moscow and St. Petersburg to give concerts. And once more sorrow descended on him; this time grief for those who suffered under the despotism of the czar oppressed his heart. He saw the best youth of Russia rise in revolt, only to be killed by Cossack bullets in the streets of Moscow.

It was while he was in Russia that he began to feel ill. As sickness crept on him like a stealthy enemy, he must surely have recalled that other unhappy visit to Russia when he had tossed and cried out in his delirium in the poor house of a railroad worker. This time he had money enough to permit him to consult a doctor, and when the verdict was, "long rest and no travel," he was quite glad to accept it. He went to Switzerland, and through the assistance of Princess Brancovan, he secured the Chalet Riond-Bosson near Lake Geneva and in the shadow of regal Mont Blanc.

For a holiday companion, he wanted his young son, and he and his friend, Madam Gorski, came from Paris. This was a happy reunion, one that Alfred had dreamed of for a long time. For the first time in his life, he and his father were together as constant companions. It did not take them long to become good friends, for letters had bridged the distances between them. Quiet, golden days followed. They talked of a home just for the two of them. The house would be small and the garden large enough for flowers and vegetables and fruit. There would be chicken coops and beehives and, perhaps, a goat with a tinkling bell.

Dreams do come true on occasions, for even while the father and son talked and planned, they received an opportunity to buy a farm. Ignacy Paderewski bought it, and the little home became a reality. In the clear, invigorating mountain air, Alfred's health began to improve. The marks of pain left his face, and his boyish laughter rang out clear as a bell. He and his father read together and talked of their taste in literature. They read Dante; the Polish poets—Mickiewicz, Slowacki; and Heine. The happy days glided into weeks, and Ignacy Paderewski, rested now and rejoiced in his son's improved health, resumed work on "Manru" which a German friend had asked to be allowed to produce first in Dresden.

The white chalet glistened and shone like a gem, and the hearts of the two who lived in it were as happy as the chalet was beautiful. While Alfred read in the garden or, wrapped in a blanket, sat gazing out across the blue lake to the mountains beyond, Ignacy Paderewski worked in the room on the second floor that he had arranged for a studio. There in the centre of the room, he had his books and his music notes on a table, and for hours upon hours, often until late at night, the composer sat at this table working on "Manru." He was happy; he had his son with him; they both loved their new home; and Paderewski liked his studio. He had pictures of his friends on the walls and on the piano were portraits of his dead wife and his son. For years he had been collecting Chinese works of art and many of them now graced this room. All his life Paderewski had an especial love for Chinese pictures and Chinese porcelain.

At last in January, 1901, he completed the orchestration of "Manru," his first opera, and within a few days, sent it to Dresden. He expected to have to wait for many days for news of it, he told Alfred, but no sooner had they resolved not to give way to impatience than news arrived. It was good; "Manru" was to have its premier in Dresden on May the twenty-ninth.

The story of the opera was taken from *The Cottage Beyond the Village,* a novel by the Polish novelist, Kraszewski. Manru, the hero, had the roving heart of a gypsy. Though he loved Ulana, the lovely girl who became his wife, he could not resist the mischievous charm of the gypsy, Asa, who persuaded him to leave Ulana and go on a voyage round the world. The witch, Urok, took pity on the mourning and deserted wife and killed Manru. Then, indeed, Ulana's heart was broken and in her grief she flung herself into a mountain lake. A dramatic story, surely, and the gypsy music was swift and rhythmic and passionate. The gentle and sad duets were as simple as the story, and quite as moving. The sweet tones of the violin blended the melodies into an easily understood unity.

The twenty-ninth of May came and "Manru" was produced in Dresden. The well-known critic, Frederic Hegar, said of the music of the opera, "It is astonishing in its steady growth, its climactic power; the second act, lyrical and increasingly dramatic; the third act, poignant and truly superb."

The success of "Manru" in Dresden resulted in the composer being sought in his peaceful seclusion, and asked to leave it for the concert platform again. The invitations were urgent and flattering. The Academy of St. Cecilia in Rome wanted to hear him play, and Queen Margherita of Italy requested him to give a concert in the royal palace. The invitations were so imperative that he said farewell to his son and his haven in the Alps. He went not only to Rome but to many other cities in Italy, and everywhere he went, he was acclaimed enthusiastically. When he left the country, the station platform in Rome was thronged with members of the royal family and of the aristocracy of Italy, gathered to say farewell and to ask him to return.

From Italy he went to the ancient city of Bilbao in Spain. He was preparing for a concert when a telegram was handed to him: "Alfred has died. Come at once."

Once more death had robbed him. He had left his son this time with a light heart, for the boy, then twenty years old, had appeared stronger than ever before in his short life. He had laughed with his father and they had talked of the time when Alfred would go with him on his tours.

"After this famous doctor in Augsburg has given me his new treatment," Alfred had said on the day they had parted, "then I shall surely be strong enough to accompany you everywhere, even to America."

But Alfred had died on the way to Augsburg, and once more Ignacy Paderewski's dream of a happy family life was shattered. His wife was dead; his father was dead; and now Alfred. The sparkle of fun and youthful eagerness left his eyes and they became shaded with coldness. Streaks of gray appeared in his golden hair and deep lines of sorrow robbed his face of its vital "joy-of-living" expression. The keyboard was all that was left to him.

Alfred Paderewski was buried in the cemetery at Montmorency, not far from Paris, and his father returned to the little chalet near Geneva alone. Never again, he thought, would he be able to write music about his own happiness—or his own sorrow—for this grief had turned his heart to ice. The black and white keys of his piano would sing the songs of other lives—but never his.

Twelve

Cocky Robert of Australia

When Ignacy Paderewski finally left his Swiss chalet after the death of his son, it was to go to Australia and New Zealand. On this journey the pianist was accompanied by his wife, who before their marriage had been Madam Gorski and for many years Alfred's friend, nurse, and companion. They sailed in the month of May, just after spring had come to the valleys and the sunny mountain slopes, and after a voyage of thirty-five days they arrived in Melbourne. It was mid-July and midwinter.

His first concert in Australia was given in Melbourne, and soon requests for concerts came from every part of the vast land. His managers, Mr. Adlington and Mr. Lemmone, had no difficulty in planning an extensive tour, for each concert was the forerunner of more invitations. Their problem was one of choosing the places where the most people would be privileged to hear the renowned pianist. The governors of New South Wales, South Australia, and Queensland opened their homes to him, and he was received with as great enthusiasm as he had been in the capitals of Europe.

A difficulty, such as had never confronted him before, presented itself in Australia. It was one that caused him many rueful smiles and many exclamations of irritation, and he never forgot it. The members of the orchestra that accompanied him belonged to a musicians' union. Their working day was eight hours—no more. Would they play an encore? Yes, if there was time within their eight hours. And as for practice periods! Poor Mr. Paderewski found himself in a constant whirl of clock-watching and waiting. When he wanted the orchestra to practise with him, every member was willing, provided it was neither lunch-time, dinner-time, nor end of the eight-hour-day-time. Signor Hazon and his union orchestra—Ignacy Paderewski never forgot them.

An Australian friend went on tour with him, and he never forgot him, either. He was Cocky Robert, a parrot with magnificent plumage and a delightful and often appropriate vocabulary. Cocky Robert was given to Mr. Paderewski by Mr. Lemmone, the concert manager of Melbourne, on the day the pianist left Australia for New Zealand. The little fellow proved to be an entertaining companion, although at times he caused his master some embarrassment. He may not have been as affectionate as Siwek, the pet of his childhood, but what he lacked in affection was compensated for by his loyalty. For a long time Cocky Robert was the "hero" of some of Mr. Paderewski's best anecdotes.

There was, for instance, the time he escaped from his cage in a New Zealand hotel and pursued his master, who was being driven to the hot springs. Neither driver not passenger was aware of his presence until Cocky Robert, perched on the cover top of the carriage, cried out, "Look here, you must have a drink. Do have a drink."

The Maori driver drew his reins, a little startled by this sudden and urgent invitation, and answered in a dignified voice, "Thank you, sir, but I had a drink just before I left home."

The hot springs of Rotorua in New Zealand are famous the world over for their health-giving qualities and while he was resting in that beautiful land, Mr. Paderewski went to them frequently. While he was there he met and became friends with Miss Maggie Papakura, a Maori woman, famed for her cooking.

One day Miss Maggie escorted Mr. Paderewski and a group of his friends to the Lake of Rotorua. The waters of this lake are as cold as ice, but on an island set in the middle of the dark blue expanse of water, there are geysers from which boiling water and steam gush and rise high in the air.

As they stood looking at the water and steam soaring into the air, Miss Maggie said, "Now I shall cook your dinner."

Cook dinner! But how? She knew exactly what to do. Her fame, in fact, had been achieved by this particular skill. First, she strung fish, caught in the icy waters of Lake Rotorua, on long weeds and thrust this "line" into the geyser. Next, she selected fresh native fruits for cooking, and these she treated as she had the fish. Only one member of the party, Madam Paderewski, did not enjoy the unusual dinner, and Miss Maggie spread a feast of fresh, but uncooked, pineapple, bananas, and oranges for her.

Not long after his visit to the geysers in the midst of Lake Rotorua, Mr. Paderewski learned of the crowning achievement of Miss Maggie Papakura. She had escorted an English noble-man to the island, and prepared so delicious a dinner for him that he persuaded her to marry him.

There is no record of whether Cocky Robert accompanied Mr. Paderewski on his visit to Lake Rotorua or not, but prob-ably special precautions were taken to lock him securely in his cage. However, when the musician returned from the expedi-tion, Cocky Robert was on hand to encourage him as he practised. He perched on his master's shoulder, and swayed back and forth with the musician as he played, and often the parrot would cry out, "How beautiful! How beautiful!"

If Mr. Paderewski practised for a whole day, Cocky Robert stayed with him, never leaving his "post" on the musician's shoulder. When the day's work was done and the master drew a deep sigh of weariness, so did Cocky Robert, and sometimes he would express his exhaustion by wailing in a weird, shrill voice that pleased his master, but that made most listeners shudder.

On his return from the antipodes, Mr. Paderewski stayed for a short time in San Francisco, and one day he and Cocky Robert went driving beyond the city. The driver took them along a rough and exceedingly bumpy road. Cocky Robert

Mr. Paderewski when he was forty years of age

did not like being jostled about and he was quick to observe, apparently, that his master was not enjoying being flung from one side of the buggy to the other, so he administered a rebuke to the driver.

"You wretch, you wretch!" he screamed in his loudest voice, "Go to the devil!"

The driver stopped his horse instantly. He looked at Mr. Paderewski, then stepped down from the carriage, and led his horses over the road until he could find a good turning place. When he resumed his seat in the buggy, he guided his team very carefully to a better road. Mr. Paderewski apologized for his parrot's mischievous tongue, and once the driver knew that the reprimand had come from his feathered passenger, he laughed and accepted the scolding with very good grace.

Cocky Robert was to have one more opportunity of rescuing his master from annoyance in San Francisco, and this he achieved with no tact but with complete success. A group of newspaper reporters called on Mr. Paderewski at his hotel, among them a woman who hurled a flood of questions at the musician, each one a little more pointless and stupid than its predecessor. Mr. Paderewski's patience was almost exhausted and he cast a hurried, urgent glance at Cocky Robert, sitting on the sofa beside him.

The bird took it as a signal. He flapped his wings, swooped close to the woman, and then, when she showed no sign of restraining her questions, he walked under her chair and cried out in a lusty voice that was heard by everyone in the room, "Go away! I don't like your voice. Go away, I say."

And the woman did as she was told. She gathered up her

notebook, pencils, and gloves in an instant, and darted from the room so fast that no one could stop her. She did not hear Mr. Paderewski's hasty apology. Nothing but the suppressed laughter of her colleagues reached her ears.

It would be easy to fill many pages with anecdotes of Cocky Robert, but these few are enough to show that he was a loyal and amusing companion. It was not hard to apologize for his misdemeanors, for usually they resulted in laughter in which the bird shared as gaily as his master and his friends.

Cocky Robert went with his master to the Chalet Riond-Bosson in Switzerland, and there continued to be the musician's protector and companion. But one day he encountered a defense problem that was too much for him. A cow sauntered close to the garden gate, and moo-ed a loud greeting or an insistent request for admission. Mr. Paderewski was practising and Cocky Robert observed that the bellowing annoyed him, so he decided to teach the cow a lesson. He dashed out of the open window, and circled about the animal madly, scolding all the time. At first the cow ignored the stormy bird, but not for long, for Cocky Robert would not be ignored. They began to fight, and alas, the odds were against the parrot. After half an hour of wing flapping and sharp pecking on Cocky Robert's part, and tail swishing, horn ramming, and kicking from the cow, the parrot fell, a weary and breathless bunch of feathers. Cocky Robert was dead.

(One record says that Cocky Robert died of pneumonia sometime after this encounter, and while Mr. Paderewski was on a concert tour.)

Thirteen

The March of War

Ignacy Paderewski was sitting on the red and gold sofa in his studio, reading *La Gloria de Don Ramiro,* written by the Argentinian writer, Enrique Rodriguez Larreta, a friend of many years standing. As he read, the world of reality vanished, and his quiet room became thronged with bold-eyed, dashing knights attired in uniforms of many colors. The rafters rang with the vigorous roll of their songs and the powerful call of their army trumpets. If the pale Swiss sun peeping in at the windows could have had a glimpse of the splendor and strength that, in imagination, surrounded the musician, it surely would have hidden its face in shame, for it had no warmth to pour into the room. But at this moment Ignacy Paderewski had no need for the sun's brightness; he

113

was completely oblivious to the stirring, chill wind that drifted in from the mountains, for he was under the spell of the tale. Deep, lusty, reckless laughter—what a book it was!

The world of reality had vanished from the studio, but not from the kitchen downstairs. There, in the brick-floored domain of the housekeeper, urgent and exciting business was in progress. The day was July thirty-first, St. Ignacy's day, and a sumptuous feast was being prepared for friends of Ignacy Paderewski. This was the year 1914, and if the pianist, lost in the pages of a romantic Spanish tale, had returned to thoughts of his own life, he surely would have recalled many of the days of his patron saint. The day in Sudylkow, for instance, when he had led his small companions to the meadow to watch him feed cookies to his horse, Siwek, and they had seen the Cossacks go riding by and disappearing in the dust and the distance. The day in Warszawa, when he and Tosia and his father had gone to a concert. Oh, there were many days of the good saint that he could have recalled, had he been able to tear himself away from his book. But he read on, and Madam Helena, in the kitchen, bustled from table to stove, determined to have her eyes on every happening. She tasted food, approved or frowned stern dissatisfaction; she arranged decorations, set out trays, and ordered the servants in a firm, not-to-be-disobeyed voice. The commotion in the kitchen was very great, as it had every right to be, of course, for the party was to be very great. Exceedingly important—those were the words Madam Helena used when she urged the servants to more speed and greater care.

Exceedingly important, indeed, for guests were coming from

Berlin, from London, from Paris, from New York—from the very ends of the earth, the busy servants must have thought as Madam Helena enumerated the countries from which they were coming. And they were coming to the Chalet Riond-Bosson at Morges for one purpose—to do honor to the great musician, Paderewski, who was also a sincere friend. The sun must have lost some of her haughty manner when the guests began to arrive. Her countenance must have expanded into a warm smile, for these people were really illustrious—the kind upon whom the sun had smiled with marked graciousness.

At last the master wearied of the stormy cavalcade that marched through the pages of his book, and laid it down with a sigh. The sunbeams, playing hide-and-seek over the crimson carpet of the studio, beckoned him to the window. From its deep sill he leaned far out, looking to the hills and mountains that rolled and billowed to the deep blue sky. The air that he drew into his lungs in long, deep breaths was clear and cold, frosted by the mountains from which it came in a sweeping wind. The sun, still pale, glinted momentarily on a white-capped peak, but before the snow became dazzling, it was hidden by a soft gray cloud. Now it came out again, peeping like a mischievous child from behind the skirts of its mother. The pianist saw it all—the rugged grandeur and the gentle, delicate beauty—and then he turned to the piano.

Melodies closely akin to the scene before him were drifting through his mind, and he began to put them into sound. They came slowly, and soon, as he played, the mountains of Switzerland, the uncertain sunshine, the studio itself, gave place to a tender, haunting melody that rose from a sob to a painful cry, and then sank to steady weeping. Now the mournful quality was lost in a melody of tender reminiscence. The great Paderewski loved to recall the days of his childhood, for in his recollections he found courage to carry on the tasks that talent and ambition had put upon him. So now into his improvising came memories of Sudylkow and of children walking through the mud that was like bread dough—and other memories, too—of Cossacks riding through the village, of workers trudging home to their poor cottages at the end of the day, of holidays and merry-making and his sister Antonina playing the piano. Siwek, the pet of his childhood, was woven into the rhythm, and so were the swaying trees of the forest and the sweet fragrance of violets and wild roses.

There was an abrupt knock on the door. The first guest had arrived at the Chalet Riond-Bosson. He was the sculptor, Wiwulski, to whom, four years before, Paderewski had given an important commission. It was to erect a monument in honor of the Polish victory over the Teutons at the Battle of Grunwald in the year 1410. Ever since his tenth year, when he had read of the victory in a book his father had given him, he had planned to have the monument built in the ancient city of Krakow. On the five hundredth anniversary of the victory, July the fifteenth, 1910, Paderewski had commissioned the work to be done, and now the magnificent structure, designed by Wiwulski, stood in Poland's old capital.

More guests had arrived while Paderewski and Wiwulski were talking. Their laughter and cordial greetings came up to the studio from the hall below, and the musician hurried down to welcome them. He shook hands first with Felix Weingartner, the conductor, who had come with his wife, quite as renowned for her jewels as her husband was for conducting orchestras. Two talented brothers stood a little withdrawn from the others; they were the brothers Morax—Jean, the painter, and Rene, the dramatist—and as was usual, they were deep in an argument. Mr. and Mrs. Sembrich were discussing the growth of artistic consciousness in America with Mr. and Mrs. Ernest Schelling. Gustave Doret, the Swiss composer, was at the piano, playing snatches of his latest composition for Timothy Adamowski and L. G. Sharpe, a concert manager from London. Miss Alma-Tadema, the daughter of the English artist who had painted Mr. Paderewski more than a decade before, sat in a corner, making sketches of various guests.

After Mr. Paderewski had shaken the hand of each of his guests, the sculptor Wiwulski came with a tray filled with glasses of champagne. When each guest had taken one, Mr. Wiwulski called for a toast.

"A toast to our friend and host, Ignacy Paderewski," he proclaimed.

"To his health!" a chorus of voices shouted.

Ignacy Paderewski smiled and tried to make a speech, but he could not. His heart was too full. So instead of expressing his gratitude in words, he did it in handclasps. He went again from guest to guest. Then he sat down at the piano and played parts of his "Maytime Album." He changed to "Song of Love," and from it drifted to a playful scherzo. After he had played a barcarole that he had heard a gondolier play in

Vienna, he began the waltz "Caprice," and nodded to his guests to dance.

They danced and as they danced, they sang. Their joyous music drifted out into the blue Swiss night and down into the little village where storekeepers and tourists paused to listen to it. Several curious ones stole up the pathway to the entrance gate, and stood there listening and looking at the sparkle of lights and jewels.

After dinner, the sumptuous dinner that Madam Helena had taken such care to have as perfect as possible, the guests played cards and talked politics. Their faces became anxious when they touched on the ominous situation that had loomed up in Europe within the last few weeks. It had grown serious within the week; even now it might—no, surely not—have grown to a real threat of war.

The Swiss night had been driven beyond the Alps and the timid light of the dawn had touched the mountain peaks with delicate tones of pink, before the guests began to murmur that they must leave. When the sounds of cow and goat bells, ringing clearly in the brisk morning air, reached them, they began to move toward the door of the drawing-room. It was at this moment, this time between night and day, that the dreadful news came. A herdsman had got it at the railway station or the post office—no matter which—and given it to the cook. Soon messengers came rushing to the chalet with telegrams. Imperative summons had come from Paris, from Berlin, and from London.

What had happened? The dreadful threat had become a reality. War had come to Europe. War.

The guests hesitated no longer. They hurried for their wraps. There was not a moment to lose. How far away their native lands seemed at that moment! The guests from Paris stared at those from Berlin, and shuddered. They could not believe it, but they knew that it must be true, for it had been hanging over them for days.

Ignacy Paderewski went out to the balcony to wave farewell to his departing friends, and from there, he called after them in a ringing, hopeful voice, "This war may bring freedom to those who have hungered for it for decades. Think of the Lithuanians, the Ukrainians, the Poles. The heel of the oppressor has been on them for a long time."

There was more to his speech, but it was lost in a burst of applause from the people standing, white and fearful, at the gate, waiting for their carriages. As they drove away, they heard the music of a vigorous military march. Paderewski had gone to his piano and was sending this farewell to them.

The departing visitors heard its thunderous notes. So did the people in the neighboring chalets. So did the forest trees. So did the mighty Alps. It was the music of marching feet, of people crying out for freedom, of peasants rising in revolt. The music rolled out like a battle cry, and the people who heard it felt strong and ready for the stupendous struggle before them.

After the march was done, Ignacy Paderewski stood in the doorway of his chalet and said aloud, "the day of freedom may be dawning for Poland."

Fourteen

The Battle for Freedom

When Ignacy Paderewski came to New York in 1915, there was one man, above all others, whom he wanted to see. He wanted to see him because he thought that he would understand the condition of Poland and that through him, he could present Poland's cause to President Woodrow Wilson. The man was Colonel Edward House, who was the adviser and friend of the President of the United States. He was a man who had an intimate knowledge of European conditions; he had just been appointed the President's personal representative to the European Governments. Later, Prime Minister Georges Clemenceau of France was to say of him, "He is a super-civilized person who escaped from the wilds of Texas; he sees everything and understands everything . . . He has a sifting, pondering mind."

Long before Clemenceau, "the tiger of France," wrote this description of him, Colonel House was internationally known for his insight into world affairs. When Ignacy Paderewski had visited at the home of Lord Northcliffe in London, he had heard this American spoken of as one of the most reliable thinkers of the time. At Lord Northcliffe's home, Paderewski had met an American, Carl Vrooman, and now on his arrival in New York, he asked Mr. Vrooman to assist him in presenting the case of Poland to this great American statesman. Mr. Vrooman probably knew how well the Polish pianist had pleaded his country's cause in London, for he immediately introduced him to Robert W. Wooley, who told Colonel House of Mr. Paderewski's wish to see him.

"Yes, I'll see him," Mr. House said to Mr. Wooley. "I'll see him to-day, this morning."

Mr. Wooley hurried to the Gotham Hotel where Mr. Paderewski was living, and his news that a meeting with Colonel House had been arranged, brought tears to the musician's eyes. He not only shook Mr. Wooley's hand, but kissed him effusively, and exclaimed over and over again, "My country will be free! I know! I know! America will help us. There will be a free Poland."

All the way to Colonel House's home, which was on East Fifty-third Street, Mr. Paderewski kept up a stream of delighted words. He was too excited to talk in sentences, but spoke in little bursts: "Bread. Shirts. Medicine. Poles in Chicago. In Detroit. Everywhere Poles work. A better to-morrow."

Even if Mr. Wooley had wanted to stop him, he could not

have done so. Mr. Paderewski's enthusiasm could not have been restrained. As he talked, he flung his arms up and out. He must have looked like a human windmill rushing down Fifth Avenue, his hair and necktie flying in the breeze.

Once within Colonel House's library, Mr. Paderewski became somewhat calmer, and settled down to a conversation that lasted several hours. He told a little of his country's past and her subservience to foreign countries. He described the patriotism that burned like a constant flame in the heart of all true Poles. He told of their willingness to fight and of how, even then, they were fighting for freedom.

With a sad face and a tremor in his voice, he said, "Poland needs a million dollars. Her country is ruined. Her people are starving."

"There is no legal Polish government," one of the listeners pointed out. "Do you expect the United States to lend money in such great sums to a relief committee. Who will pay her back?"

"We Poles will pay her back," Mr. Paderewski answered instantly and with fine pride in his voice. "Never, never, will we forget our debt to the United States. Our hearts will always be warm to the people of America. No other country has done such a noble thing. She will be trusted by all the freedom-loving people in the world."

Mr. Wooley, seeing how excited Mr. Paderewski was becoming again, tried to restrain him, but Colonel House whispered, "Give him a chance to explain. What he says is very interesting."

So the conversation continued. Mr. Paderewski reminded

his two listeners of what the Americans of Polish descent were doing. They were collecting money and buying clothes and food and medical supplies for their brothers in Europe. Chicago and Detroit and many small cities, as well, were seething with work. Colonel House listened and then asked questions about Poland. What was the condition of the city worker? Of the peasant? Was the soil fertile? Were the people united? By his questions the American showed that he was not only interested but much disposed in Poland's favor.

"Is this effort to gain Poland's freedom your idea entirely," Colonel House asked, "or are others working, too, with the same fervor?"

"Yes, yes, indeed," Paderewski answered, eager to tell of his countrymen's efforts. "Polish patriots have organized relief committees in London and Paris. All Poles, all true Poles, are ready to give their lives for our country. In London G. K. Chesterton is working for us. So is Lord Balfour. So are Prime Minister Asquith and Wickham Stead, the journalist. Miss Lawrence Alma-Tadema has written a book about Poland."

As Colonel House sat in thought for a moment, Mr. Paderewski continued, "I interested her father in Poland many years ago, when I first went to Paris" and, with a rueful smile, "I haven't paid her yet for the portrait her father painted of me."

The visit came to an end and when Colonel House was bidding his guests good-bye, he said, "At last I understand Poland's situation clearly, and I must say that I like the struggle you are making. Do not worry too much. This oppression cannot continue. Poland's future is brightening."

This first visit to Colonel House was the beginning of a friendship between the two men. After that, they often walked together in Central Park and as they walked, they talked of a new world that might be dawning for oppressed peoples. Colonel House talked with great deliberation, weighing his words carefully before saying them. Ignacy Paderewski spoke with feverish eagerness; he hurled his words from his lips at the rate of several hundred a minute, so it seemed to a listener, and gesticulated almost as swiftly. Nevertheless, the two, so vastly different in temperament, had a great deal in common: they both loved their respective countries and both esteemed their brother citizens. It is little wonder that their friendship was sincere and lasting.

Fifteen

A Visit to President Wilson

The war in Europe, begun in the summer of 1914, was still raging in the autumn of 1915. The enemy had come perilously close to Paris. On calm, clear nights London could hear the rumble of guns. Troops from every part of the world had embarked from their home ports and gone to take up the battle on the sodden fields of France and Belgium. Men had died and were dying by the thousands. Little children were crying for food. The tragic condition of the world was filling the hearts of human beings with grief, and yet, when the mellow autumn days came to New Jersey, it would have been easy to forget the misery that had sunk like a black cloak over Europe.

Easy to forget? Well, not for Ignacy Paderewski, for although his nostrils drew in the luscious fragrance of ripening apples and plums, and his eyes rejoiced at the sight of the rich golds and browns of autumn, his heart was heavy with the misery of the world. He knew that children were crying for food in Poland and in all Europe. In imagination, that persistent wailing rang in his ears, and no smile lit up his countenance on the day when he accompanied Colonel House to Long Branch, New Jersey, to visit President Woodrow Wilson.

The United States of America had not yet declared war against the aggressor nations, and in the minds and hearts of some of the most idealistic statesmen there still lingered a hope that the country could be saved from war. The thought was not associated with one of aloofness or with a resolution to ignore the devastation of Europe, but with the idea that America might do something to stop the spreading chaos.

With this thought in their minds, patriots of many nations gathered around President Wilson to present the views of their respective countries and to beg him for his assistance in the struggle to release Europe from the devilish clutch of war. Ignacy Paderewski was one of these. More than two decades before, he had first come to America, known then as a pianist only; now all America was coming to know him as a zealous patriot.

On this autumn day he sat in President Wilson's quiet study, and talked of his country and his people. He touched on her past; he may have mentioned the ancient battle of Grunwald; he told of her kings and of how some of them had broken faith with their people; perhaps he described his own childhood experience with Cossacks; certainly he told of the part Poland was taking in the war then raging in Europe. As he talked in his full, musical voice, occasionally pausing for the exact word to convey his meaning, President Wilson listened attentively, his keen eyes observing the expressions that moved rapidly over Mr. Paderewski's face. Sometimes there was a gentle, reminiscent smile but it never lingered for long, for stern resolution was in his voice and it showed on his brow and on his lips, even in the firm set of his shoulders.

When Mr. Paderewski was finished, President Wilson rose from his desk, and walked about the room for a few seconds. He paused to look out on the lawn and the fertile fields, so calm and so quiet—so far removed from the devastation of war. Then he turned back to his guest, and standing by his desk, began to talk slowly and firmly. It was easy for his listeners to know that what he was saying had been in his mind for a long time.

"Not only your country, but all Europe, must have a new order," President Wilson said, "and not Europe only, but the whole world. Gold must not be the master, nor powerful nations. Man's happiness—that should be the keynote of our new world. In a free country everyone must have an equal chance, without regard to race, color, or creed. There must be one law for everyone."

When the President paused to clear his throat and take a drink of water, Mr. Paderewski said in a voice made timid by the emotion that was welling up in him, "I am indeed happy to hear this humanistic idea of yours. It is splendid. Magnificent!"

"The countries that believe this," the President resumed, standing straight and tall as a Greek statue, "should unite to form a League of Nations and that league should have the same democratic ideals as the countries represented in it. For instance, a country of ten million would select ten representatives, while a country of forty millions would have forty representatives."

The President paused again and looked toward his listeners for approbation or suggestion. When he saw that Mr. Paderewski's face was wreathed in a smile of delighted satisfaction, he told more of the plan that had been evolving in his mind: the small state should have the same weight as the large, for each would have but one vote; when disputes arose, a special tribunal would decide; no problem could go beyond this special tribunal for there would be no higher court.

The President expressed more ideas on the subject, and one, in particular, brought an enthusiastic nod of approval from his guest—the league should have a police force to safeguard its member nations from one another and from threatening outsiders. Mr. Paderewski knew Europe and its multitude of problems well enough to know that some visible show of force was likely to be necessary.

"If only this could happen now," he sighed. "Now, yes, now, and save the world from increasing pain. Brute strength vanquished; greed vanquished; the good of the people to be the basis for laws."

The President wiped the perspiration from his furrowed brow, and said, "When it comes, Poland will have the same power as Russia, Germany, and Great Britain."

A tender smile flickered on Mr. Paderewski's face as he said, "If only she can free herself from her enslavement!"

"We will help her," Colonel House, who had been silent

during most of the conversation, exclaimed now. "Your country shall again have a beautiful spring; she shall have freedom."

Mr. Paderewski was about to speak when the President interrupted with a request. "Perhaps you will play Chopin's 'Polonaise Militaire' for me now," he said.

So Ignacy Paderewski went to the piano, and played the music that has been a source of inspiration to hundreds of great men the world over. His strong, graceful fingers seemed like fairies dancing over the keyboard. The face of the musician, as he played, was suffused with a warm, almost happy smile. The conversation with the President and the music of the great master, Chopin, had combined to raise his spirits to a degree of hopefulness that he had seldom felt since the war in Europe had grown so bitter and so cruel. A bright light was coming through the gloom, a light that would show the way to bread and justice for all the peoples of the world; this was the thought in Mr. Paderewski's mind as he played for President Wilson on that autumn day in the year 1915.

President Wilson kept his word to Ignacy Paderewski. As he and his colleagues planned and talked of a new world in which peace, not war, would dominate and in which all peoples should have "bread and justice," he never forgot Poland, the country that for more than a century had been under the rule of a foreign power. On January the eighth, 1918, *it* happened. Poles, who had long been in exile, read of it and rejoiced. They felt that now, at last, the release, for which they and their ancestors had struggled, was about to come to their country. This was read in Congress:

"An independent Polish State should be erected which should include the territories inhabited by indisputably Polish population, which should be assured of a free and secure access to the sea, and whose political and economical independence and territorial integrity should be guaranteed by international covenant."

This was a triumph for Ignacy Paderewski and for Poland. It was, too, a triumph for Americans of Polish descent, for they, though they loved their new country and were happy in the comfortable homes they and their parents had built in America, had never forgotten their brothers in Europe. Polish Americans who worked in factories and offices and on farms rejoiced in this promise of freedom, and in doing so they paid honest tribute to the patriot who had helped to bring it about. On the day that Ignacy Paderewski left New York to return to Poland, some said to be king, and others, to be the prime minister of a democratic republic, they left their work, and went to wish him *bon voyage*.

Ignacy Paderewski stood on the top deck of the ship, and waved his hands in farewell. A steady, vigorous breeze blew his hair over his face, and as he pushed it back, he shouted, "Until we meet again, my friends. I am going now to fulfil my obligations to my countrymen."

There was more shouting, more hand-waving, more breezes blowing steadily like a vigorous march, and then the ship's whistles announced the ship's departure.

"*La patrie avant tout*," Mr. Paderewski said to the mustached French general, standing beside him on the deck.

"*L'art ensuite*," the general said.

Sixteen

New Year in Warszawa

The whole country of Poland was held fast in winter's grip, —a friendly winter it was, for snow sparkled in the sunshine and the trees, so dark and so white, looked as if they were decorated for Christmas. The shores of the Baltic were like crystal, and when the sun shone on them, they were as though lighted by a hundred tiny flames—some delicate pink, some blue, shot with pale green. On Christmas day in this year 1918, the ship on which Ignacy Paderewski was a passenger docked at Gdansk, the old port of Poland. From there, he hurried to Poznan for a conference with the heads of the nation, and now on New Year's day, 1919, he had come to Warszawa and was registered at the Hotel Bristol.

The streets of the city were decorated with red and white flags, and were thronged with people who had braved the icy winds to welcome Paderewski. Faces were happy;

voices were vibrant with eagerness; everyone felt that something most remarkable was just about to happen. Few if any of the people realized, at the moment, that the wintry breezes were blowing through their thin coats as if they were no more than paper. They shivered, yes, and blew their breath on their chapped hands, but they laughed, too, and sang national songs that had not been heard for a long time in the old streets of Warszawa. They sang songs of their fields and of the men and women who worked in them; they sang songs of their winding river, Wisla, and of her bargemen; they sang songs of their factories and of the workers. When the wind swept over them in rude gusts, they, still singing, began to dance. All Warszawa was filled with delirious joy and the participants in the joy had come from various parts of Poland to share in it.

"Poland is to be governed by peasants and workers," a man, whose smudgy face and grimy clothes proclaimed him to be a coal-heaver, announced with assurance. "And why shouldn't she be, tell me that, when ninety percent of her people are workers and peasants?"

"You are right," one person and another answered. "Workers and peasants are the ones who have suffered. They know how work should be distributed. They know the meaning of justice." This was followed by hand-clapping and more songs, many more songs.

"It does not matter to me who governs in Warszawa," a woman with a baby wrapped in a shawl said, "so long as I get milk for my children. I want work; my husband wants work; then our children will not cry for milk and bread.

See!" And she drew attention to the pale face of the baby she held in her arms.

"I can't give you work, madam," a man in the throng exclaimed, "for I have none myself, but I will get you milk now for that poor youngster."

And off he went, elbowing his way through the throng, and returned in a few minutes with a tall mug of milk.

"That is the kind of man who should head our new country," a man, who was something of a philosopher, said to the mother of the baby. "You see, he is ready to serve and to share. He has no work, yet he gets food for a hungry child." The baby was now drinking the milk greedily.

"Paderewski is going to be the head of our government, the king perhaps," a woman close at hand said in a low ringing voice.

"Our king!" one person and another exclaimed, and there was scorn in the voices. "Do you think that all we need is a king? We have had enough of them."

"You are right," a multitude of voices called out. "No more kings for Poland. We are to be a republic with a president. You'll see."

"But what have you against Paderewski?" a woman asked a little impatiently. "Is he not a great patriot? Has he not worked for us in America?"

"Yes! Yes!" the throng cried out. "We've nothing against Paderewski. It's just that we don't like kings."

"No king for Poland," many people said together and there was firm resolve in the voices.

One man who had been in America told his neighbors that

Americans would call a man like Paderewski "a swell guy." The unfamiliar words passed from one to another, and a shout, "He's a swell guy," rose like a refrain.

Before it drifted away, someone began to talk seriously of the possibility of a king.

"We have had more than three dozen kings," the man said. "Some big, some small; some were sweet, and some were bitter. Some of the country's worst degradation came from kings—."

The man's voice was drowned by an argument that arose now. There were shouts for a king; there were lusty, scornful shouts for no king. A fight might have ensued if some wise person had not started a song. In the full, lusty song the question of a king and no king was forgotten.

Excitement and merrymaking surged through the Hotel Bristol. Upstairs, downstairs—everywhere, and especially in the vast reception room where Ignacy Paderewski stood receiving friends. Officers of high military rank were there; so were noblemen and prominent citizens. There were many greetings, many smiles, and much conversation that was serious. A pause came when a boy and a girl, each about ten years of age, walked toward the pianist. The boy was dressed in a white Krakowski homespun coat, embroidered in red. He wore high leather boots that were polished until they shone like burnished metal. A red and white four-cornered hat, adorned with a brilliant peacock feather, was perched on his head. The girl wore a Lowicki costume—a gathered skirt, striped red and white, a white blouse, and a red jacket covered with embroidery. She had on high laced boots and a brightly colored kerchief was on her head and tied under her chin.

"We bring you the New Year's greeting of our new country," the boy said in a ringing voice to the smiling Mr. Paderewski.

After he had spoken, he scattered a handful of wheat, rye, barley, and oats at the musician's feet. These were the grains that grew in Poland and the gesture conveyed a wish for plenty. It was an ancient custom and one dearly loved in all the country.

"With the New Year, we wish you success and we wish that sadness may never fill your heart and that your soul will always be flooded with sunshine," the girl said, standing about five paces from Mr. Paderewski.

Then the two, the boy and the girl, said in unison, "Live long for us and for the good of our country."

The girl gave Mr. Paderewski a bouquet of flowers and after she had curtsied, the two again began to speak, this time to recite the poem, "I despise," written by Jan Kasprowicz, one of Poland's famous poets. There were few in the gathering who knew that this was one of Mr. Paderewski's favorite poems and that almost every morning he said it to himself as one says a prayer. Each said alternate lines:

"I despise those people who have no fire in them,
   No fire.
I despise those in whose hearts the spark dies,
   Spark dies.
Because they are like creatures in the grave,
   With lifeless bones.
Away from the sun that warms and shines
   And blazes."

Other lines followed rapidly and with each one spoken, the childish voices rose to the high ceiling. Their confidence was growing; they had lost the nervousness that at first had made their voices sound stifled. They were enjoying the ceremony now.

"No need to waken them in the early morning,
　To waken them." The boy almost shouted,
　fine scorn in his voice.
"Nor to bother their hearts with high hopes,
　Animal hearts." The girl was no less disdainful.
The two now joined forces to say vigorously:
"They are like pygmies in the shell of a snail,
　Ending a peaceful existence.
　While others sacrifice their lives for the truth."

As the children recited these lines from the poet's *Vale of Struggle,* an air of solemnity spread through the hall. Some bowed their heads; others looked strong and valiant like warriors taking up a noble battle; and some, like the pianist and patriot, Ignacy Paderewski, wept and made no effort to hide their tears. They were tears of happiness and hope and brotherly love.

That evening a great feast was spread in the Hotel Bristol. The guests of honor were the children who had stood in front of the hotel with their parents and who, with them, had saluted Mr. Paderewski. The host was Mr. Paderewski himself. And the feast was something more than any child had ever dreamed of. There was candy, rich American chocolate candy. There were cookies—and cakes—and tarts. There were fruits—rosy, Polish apples, oranges from Northern Africa, bananas from the Indies. Such a feast, and after it was over one little boy exclaimed, "We all had as much milk as we could drink." No wonder that after this feast, the children of Poland began to call Mr. Paderewski "our Uncle Jan from America."

Seventeen

Letters

One day late in January, 1919, Colonel House and a group
of his friends were gathered around a luncheon table; once
the meal was finished they began talking of world affairs.
Several were deeply concerned with the shaping of the world's
course, now that peace had come, and all of them looked to
the colonel for information and advice. What was happening
in the Balkans, they wanted to know. What in Germany?
And in Poland—had he heard recently from his friend,
Paderewski?

When the hum of questions had subsided the colonel said
that he would like to tell them a story about Ignacy Paderewski. After he had told the story, Colonel House added, he

would answer the enquiry about Paderewski. This is the story that was told:

In the year 1903, Mr. Paderewski went to St. Petersburg at the invitation of the Imperial Society of Music. He had already won acclaim in France and Great Britain and America. In England, he had played for Queen Victoria. For this reason, perhaps, the czar of Russia commanded him to perform for him in the Imperial Palace. When the recital was over, the czar summoned the musician to his side.

"It was a pleasure to hear so great a Russian musician," he said.

"I am a Pole, your Majesty," Mr. Paderewski answered with dignity.

"There is no Poland," the czar said haughtily, "only Great Russia exists to-day."

Mr. Paderewski bowed and murmured, "I beg your pardon, your Majesty, for speaking the truth. I am a Pole."

Before the czar could speak again, the pianist hurried to the piano, and played Chopin's "Funeral March." It was not difficult for the czar to understand the significance of the "encore!"

When the story was told and it had been applauded, Colonel House said, "He has always been like that, a fiery patriot, and many of his countrymen are like him."

"True! True! A splendid reply," one guest and another exclaimed, and then waited for Colonel House to answer the enquiry about the musician, who for the present, at least, had abandoned the piano and the concert stage for the role of statesman. He was not changing from being a pianist to being a patriot, however, for all through his career he had combined the two callings—pianist and patriot.

"I have just received a letter from Mr. Paderewski," Colonel House said, "and in it he tells me much of the tragedy of his country. It is a sad letter."

Then Colonel House told that Prussian soldiers had fired on ten thousand Polish school children, parading in Poznan in honor of their country's freedom. Many children had been injured and killed and the bullets had damaged the home of the British representative, Colonel Wade. The letter told, too, of how drunken soldiers were robbing stores and homes, and of how people were dying of hunger on the streets of Polish cities.

"It is very tragic," Colonel House said, "to think that there are thirty million people eager to rebuild their country and yet . . ." He left his sentence unfinished.

This was not the first of the many letters Mr. Paderewski had sent to America after his arrival in his homeland on Christmas Day. It was just one of a number Colonel House had received. Some had been longer; several had been brief and had been cabled.

At the time there were few statesmen in America who were not conscious of the misery of Europe; many, like Colonel House, were filled with sorrow for the after-war agony of the continent, and many, like him, were working constantly to bring about better conditions. On January the twenty-second the Secretary of State, Robert Lansing, sent this cablegram to Ignacy Paderewski in Warszawa:

"The President of the United States directs me to extend

to you, as Prime Minister and Secretary of Foreign Affairs of the Provisional Polish Government, his sincere wishes for your success in the high office which you have assumed and his earnest hope that the Government of which you are a part will bring prosperity to the Republic of Poland.

"It is my privilege to extend to you at this time my personal greetings and officially to assure you it will be a source of gratification to enter into official relations with you at the earliest opportunity; to render to your country such aid as is possible at this time, as it enters upon a new cycle of independent life, will be in due accord with that spirit of friendliness which has in the past animated the American people in their relation with your countrymen.

Lansing"

In a short time after this cablegram was dispatched giving the provisional government of Poland recognition, Great Britain, France, Italy, Switzerland, and Belgium and, in rapid succession, other countries of Europe, followed the example of the United States. Poland was, at last, a free country. Her people could proclaim their citizenship with pride. They were not subjects of any foreign ruler; they were citizens of a free Poland.

The Wisla, queen of Polish rivers, sang a happy song then, for the rafts and barges were manned by citizens who went to work with a mighty will to build their country. The peasants began to build homes on land that was theirs or that they felt sure would soon be theirs. The factories in the cities awoke from their long sleep and the workers worked again and, like the peasants, they began to build homes. Children on the way to school talked the Polish language openly, with no fear of reprimand, and teachers, released from stern foreign orders, taught their pupils about their country, Poland, and had no fear to speak the names of their heroes and their poets. Ignacy Paderewski had helped to bring this dream to reality.

Eighteen

Artist and Statesman

Prime Minister Ignacy Jan Paderewski went to the Peace Conference in Paris prepared to do battle for his country, and he found the struggle no less bitter than he had anticipated. Mr. Lloyd-George of Great Britain was one of his strongest opponents. M. Clemenceau of France, although his knowledge of European geography was greater than that of Lloyd-George, was not acutely interested in the territorial re-organization of Poland, and showed that he was ready, in this particular case at least, to follow the lead of the fiery representative of Great Britain. The one person who supported Poland's Prime Minister was President Woodrow Wilson, and when Mr. Paderewski returned to Warszawa with the boundaries of the new free country assured, he gave much credit to the President of the United States.

Poland was a free country now, and most of the European

land on which Polish people lived was within the country's boundaries. This had been accomplished by Ignacy Paderewski who had spent many years of his life in his country's cause. He had won the interest and understanding of the United States; he had fought the opposition of other countries; he had, without doubt, proved himself to be an outstanding statesman. But—and here was bitter sorrow for him—no sooner had he returned home from the Peace Conference than whispering against him began in Poland.

Many political groups were formed in the country. The Polish Parliament, called the *Sejm,* approved what Paderewski had achieved at the Conference, but this approval did not silence the murmurs of dissatisfaction. They arose to open talk and then to shouts, and in some quarters, to insults and sneers.

When he and his wife, Madam Helena, went to live in the *Zamek,* which in the past had been the palace of the Polish kings, there was much head-shaking. "You see," one person said to another, "they want to be crowned. They want to be king and queen of Poland."

Prior to her marriage to Ignacy Paderewski, Madam Paderewski had been married to a musician named Gorski. By birth she was the Baroness de Rosen, and now in Warszawa some people began addressing her as "Your Highness Helena Baroness de Rosen Gorski." As Madam Paderewski had no ambition to have such a title, she found the insult hard to bear. Both she and her husband strove to ignore the insolent remarks made about them, however, and continued to live in the palace of the kings. Their faces became sad; they began to lose their trust in their friends; and their nights were sleepless.

Ignacy Paderewski was resolved to remain firm. He faced his political opponents fearlessly. When people on the street shouted, "We have had enough kings," he and his cabinet continued trying to bring about the reforms necessary for building the new country. By his actions he hoped to show the people that he had no selfish wishes for himself. He had served Poland in the past; he wanted to continue that service.

During his long sleepless nights he made brave plans for the country he loved, and some of those visions he put into music, and played them in the night. He saw fat cattle grazing in the green meadows. He saw modern farm houses being built throughout the country and, in imagination, he caught the fragrance of violets and mignonettes and camomile blooming in the gardens. He saw happiness and prosperity spreading throughout the land. Farmers worked and sold their products. Factory workers worked and received good wages so that they could live in the modern apartment houses that were being built in the cities. As for schools—into his music he put the gay laughter of children on their way to new, well-equipped schools, and he put their shouts of joy as they played with beautiful toys after school. The vision was so wonderful that Mr. Paderewski struggled to make it real.

He has left a record of a strange and lovely dream he had one night. It came after a day of much debate and argument, and he had gone to bed in the old palace, feeling more perplexed and discouraged than usual. In this dream he saw many sleek and graceful horses, Siwek, the pet of his childhood, among them, prancing and galloping in a green meadow. He saw cattle drinking from glass troughs; he saw peasants working in the fields and going in and out of large barns, covered with red and green and golden roofs. The peasants did not wear worn and tattered clothes; their shirts were new and of many colors; so were their shoes—good, substantial, comfortable shoes. In this dream he saw children playing with toys such as had never been seen in Poland, and their laughter was full and beautiful.

Such a dream! From the country it flitted to the city where new buildings shone in the sun, and rose so high that they seemed to touch the sky. The streets were lined with automobiles and people went to work and came from work happily. They went to theatres and concerts, and played with their children in the parks. And everything was glass—glass fences, glass fountains, glass staircases. And the people were young and strong.

The dream did not end here. No, indeed, for in the next swift reel of the panorama, Mr. Paderewski dreamed that he, golden-haired as in his youth, was sitting at a piano playing music that could be heard from the Baltic to the Carpathians. And the song he was playing was the song of a happy Poland.

The dream faltered, became vague, and then drifted swiftly into nothingness. The dreamer was wide awake now, and staring into the dull blue night. The cares of the day returned to him. They were like prison chains; he could not free himself of them. He rose from his bed and went to the piano to find comfort in music. He played and played and, as the music rolled out from the palace to the shores of the Wisla, these words went through his mind over and over again: "A few more years of hard work and we will reach the shores of prosperity."

Not long after this dream, the worried statesman had another one. Like the first one, it came at the end of a day crowded with argument and debates and a few pointed insults. This dream was not pleasant. There was no laughter in it, nothing but gloom and cruelty. In this dream Ignacy Paderewski saw a black object creeping through the palace. It lurked in a passageway; it stole noiselessly up a staircase. It was a queer, misshapen creature with the tail of a jackal and the black wings of a raven. When it screeched it had a wild raven's cry. In his dream Mr. Paderewski found himself confronted by this half-jackal, half-raven creature and, in desperation, he imagined that he put his piano on his back, and called out to his wife to flee with him.

He was not released from the misery of this nightmare until his military adjutant, Major Iwanowski, entered the room. Mr. Paderewski described the dream to him, and the major said that he believed it had some political significance, for General Pilsudski, the leader of the opposition, was demanding his immediate resignation.

"Hour by hour, the opposition is growing in the *Sejm*," Major Iwanowski said. "The force is so great and it is increasing so rapidly that now it looks as if both you and your cabinet will have to resign."

The two men were silent for a long time. Mr. Paderewski's head was bowed and it was easy to see that he was deep in thought.

"Ten delegates of the *Sejm*, each representing a different group, want to have a conference with you to-day," Major Iwanowski said, at last breaking the silence.

"They will ask you to do one of two things," the major continued, "either resign, or dismiss the ministers of your cabinet."

Again the silence was long. The perplexed and saddened Prime Minister leaned his head against a post of the royal bed, and thought. What should he do? For himself, he did not care, but for Poland—was it best for his country that he resign?

"If it is for the good of the country," he said firmly, "then I shall resign."

The kings of long ago may have peered down at him from their portraits, and smiled reminiscently as they watched him in his perplexity. They may have heard his deep sighs, and whispered, "Just so, we were confronted with enemies. Just so, our supporters turned from us. Just so, we sighed and prayed and begged Almighty God to help us make wise decisions."

In December, 1919, the decision was made. Ignacy Jan Paderewski resigned as Prime Minister of Poland, and in the following January began to make preparations to leave Warszawa. He was tired, so very tired, and he longed for the quiet of his home in Switzerland. There he would devote his time to the piano. He would play and compose and from the chalet's wide windows, he would look out on the tall, snow-capped peaks of the Alps. When he was strong again, and the burden that politics had put on him had vanished, he would think of concerts once more. Many concerts. After all, he was a pianist, not a politician. Pianist and patriot—these had been his roles through life, and so they must be to the end.

Nineteen

At the Railroad Station

Ignacy Paderewski and his wife left the palace of kings, and went to live in the Hotel Bristol in Warszawa. On a day in early January, they were busy packing. Open trunks and valises were standing in the sitting-room, and Madam Paderewski was rushing from one to another. They were nearly ready to be closed and locked.

"We must leave Warszawa quietly," Mr. Paderewski said thoughtfully. "People should not know when we are going."

His wife agreed. She had no wish for farewells, either.

"If there were a demonstration of any kind," Mr. Paderewski continued, "it might increase the disunity of the country. And that I could not endure. More than ever before, Poland needs harmony among her citizens."

"You are right," Madam Paderewski said. "We shall appear to be going to Krakow, but shall really go to Poznan. No one will know where we are."

"Naturally I shall have to tell Iwanowski our plans," Mr. Paderewski said, and made one more hurried tour of the rooms of their apartment. Then he sat down to wait for the porters to come for their luggage. No more than a year ago, he had received an ovation of welcome in the same hotel. The corridors had rung with cheers and applause. How swiftly the change had come! Now he was stealing away like a thief in the night from the country he loved so dearly.

As soon as they arrived at the railway station, Mr. and Mrs. Paderewski hurried through the crowd to their seats in the train. No one recognized them. They were smiling their satisfaction with this when a loud cry pierced the air. It was a ringing cry, not quite a wail and not quite a sob. It had grief and determination in it. Mr. Paderewski looked out to see if he could find out the cause for so vehement an expression of sorrow.

"It's Edek," he exclaimed, "Edek Szymanski, of all persons! What can be the matter?"

Now Edek Szymanski was no baby. He was a big, fair-haired boy of fourteen, who seldom indulged in tears, and never in public demonstrations of grief. But on this day no one could stem his sobs, not even Mr. Paderewski, who rushed from the train to try to discover the reason for Edek's sobs. In fact, Edek did not dry his eyes and smile until Mr. Paderewski had returned with him to the Hotel Bristol.

Once there, with Mr. Paderewski and his wife begging him

to explain his sorrow, Edek made a confession. Not all at once, but gradually, he told the reason for his tears. He had planned them for the purpose of keeping his friend and benefactor, Mr. Paderewski, in Warszawa. By some means which he did not tell, Edek had found out that the Paderewskis were planning to leave Poland, and had resolved that he would do his best to prevent them from doing so. Hence, the stormy, convulsive sobs.

One day passed and another, and still Mr. Paderewski was in Warszawa. His wife was becoming anxious and impatient to be away, but nothing that she said made any impression on her husband. He was not going to be hurried, for he had something very important to do before he could leave Poland.

"Edek is very much attached to me," he said. "He says that if I go over the border into another country, he will accompany me. I know we cannot take him with us, but we cannot leave until I have made arrangements for his education."

Edek Szymanski was a poor boy. His father was a laborer who lived in the Wola suburb of Warszawa. Edek peddled newspapers on the streets of the city, and on occasions he went to the war refugee shelter in Wiejska Street to recite poems he had written, at concerts given for the people who lived in this pleasant home. Madam Helena Paderewski, who took an active interest in the refugee home, had met him there and brought him to her husband's attention. Mr. Paderewski had listened to the boy recite his own poems and the poems of famous Polish poets. He had been much impressed by the boy's gift of interpretation, and sometimes had played accompaniments for his recitations.

One day after Edek had recited a poem with very deep feeling, Mr. Paderewski had whispered to his wife, "You know, that yellow-haired boy reminds me of my son, Alfred. If Alfred had been able to walk he would have been just such a boy as Edek. Alfred loved poetry, too. Remember?"

Madam Paderewski remembered very well, perhaps even better than his father remembered, for she had looked after Alfred for many years before she married his father. She had read some of the whimsical verses that Alfred had written. In fact, Alfred's yellowed notebooks were among the few treasured possessions they were taking to Switzerland with them.

It had been easy for the Paderewski's to become much interested in Edek Szymanski. He had often visited in their home, and Mr. Paderewski had spent many hours listening to him recite his poems. Sombre verses they were, all about workers and the misery of the poor, which was very natural, for from his cradle Edek had never escaped poverty.

And now the boy was adamant. He would not permit his benefactor to leave him. "Please take me with you," Edek pleaded, and if it had been possible Mr. Paderewski would surely have done so. As he felt certain that Edek would not be happy separated from his family, he made arrangements for him to continue his education. He even engaged a music teacher for him, and instructed him to play accompaniments for Edek when he recited his poems.

When the hour for farewells came, at last, Mr. Paderewski said to Edek, "Keep writing poetry, my dear boy, and send it to me in Switzerland. Be sure to work hard. Be honest and truthful."

The train whistle blared a warning of departure. There were tears in Mr. Paderewski's eyes as he said, "I have left money for postage and a little more with your aunt in Wola. Remember, send your poems to me in Switzerland."

Another shrill whistle, and Mr. Paderewski hurried on to the train. The last figure he saw in Warszawa was that of Edek Szymanski, standing on the station platform waving farewell to him.

Ignacy Jan Paderewski was leaving his country, the country that he had helped to liberate. There was deep pain in his heart as the train carried him to Switzerland. The months of his short premiership had not been happy, yet he had not found them too difficult, for he had enjoyed serving his country. His smile was sad, but it had no bitterness in it, as his wife repeated the old saying, "A prophet hath no honor in his own country." He never returned to his country's capital.

What of Edek Szymanski? As he had promised his dear friend, Mr. Paderewski, he studied hard. He graduated from the University of Warszawa, and won for himself a prominent place in the literature of modern Poland. His poems were about workers and about the freedom that seemed to many young people to be denied to Poland. They were strong and vigorous, these poems that Edek Szymanski wrote and recited to his fellow citizens. He never left Warszawa, just as his poems never left the poverty of the poor people of Poland.

On a certain September day in the year 1939, barbarians from the west marched on Warszawa where Edek Szymanski lived with his wife and two little daughters. In the second week of the siege, Edek Szymanski, whom Ignacy Paderewski loved dearly and whose career he had followed with pride, was killed defending his native city.

But his poems still live, and they are sung wherever liberty-loving Polish people lift their voices in song.

Twenty

Concerts Begin Again

Ignacy Jan Paderewski returned to his piano, and although he did not forget Poland, he made no effort to resume a place in her politics. He would always be an ardent patriot, but never a politician. He decided that he could best serve his country as an artist, and it was as an artist that he came to America toward the end of 1922, after more than two years of rest and practice in his chalet in Switzerland.

On the evening of November the twenty-second, 1922, a distinguished audience gathered in Carnegie Hall in New York City. Almost as many people crowded on Fifty-Seventh Street and the queues extended down Seventh Avenue. Then the word ran down the lines: "No more seats," and the disappointed people got into their automobiles or descended to subways. They could not hear Ignacy Paderewski on his first return concert in America.

It was a magnificent concert. Music lovers had come from all parts of the United States and Canada to hear the renowned musician. He began with a composition by Mendelssohn, and followed it with Schumann's Fantasia, Opus 17. Next came Beethoven's Sonata, Opus 57, and if one could judge from the applause, this probably was the most popular of all the selections. Yet when Paderewski began to play Chopin, the audience was spellbound. It was easy for the listener to realize that there was some special kinship between these two: Chopin, the composer, and Paderewski, the interpreter. After four selections from Chopin, the announced programme concluded with compositions of Liszt and Wagner. Then came imperative demands for encores. Shouted requests of, "Your own compositions, please," rose above the hand-clapping.

Ignacy Paderewski was never stingy with his music. He gave to his audiences generously and on this night he played a number of his minuets. For a conclusion, however, he returned to Chopin and to a selection that he played more frequently than any other—Etude in E, Opus 10.

Unlike many other artists, Paderewski was applauded not only for his music and his gracious manners, but for that quality of friendliness that was in him. When he stood before an audience, it did not seem that he was greeting a miscellaneous group of people, but a party of choice friends whom he loved dearly. His sweeping bows seemed to say to the people waiting to hear him, "I'm so happy that we are to spend some time together."

This surprising gift of taking his audiences into his confidence brought him many privileges and almost as many problems, and if the truth were known, he probably loved the problems quite as much as the privileges. When he was on his tour across America in 1923, young music lovers wrote him letters, telling him of their difficulties. Some young people even poured out the perplexities of their love affairs to him, convinced that he could give them practical advice and encouragement. His friends and members of his staff sometimes protested that these letters and visits took too much of his time, but Mr. Paderewski scorned their protests. He loved to be close to people, and frequently made notes in a diary of meetings that had given him marked pleasure.

In Minneapolis, for instance, he met two small sisters called Wanda and Helena Janowski and he was as happy to talk to them as they were to greet him. Wanda and Helena had planned their salutation to the famous pianist for a long time before he arrived in Minneapolis. They would go to his dressing-room carrying a bunch of lilies and when the door was opened they would recite poems in Polish. They carried their plan out perfectly. Mr. Paderewski listened to them recite, then asked them something about music. Their answers were correct; he talked to them a little more, and was amazed by their knowledge of music. They surprised him, too, by their ability to recite in English as well as in Polish. In a very short time the two little girls told their new friend a great deal about themselves.

No, indeed, they were not rich, Wanda and Helena told Mr. Paderewski. They had earned the money for the flowers they had brought him by running errands for their neighbors, and, on occasions, looking after babies. What were they going to do when they grew up, Mr. Paderewski asked, and the two children said shyly that they would like to be musicians. Good! Good! This pleased the noted pianist, but were they practising every day, he asked them?

"We can't," one of the girls said timidly, "because we have no piano."

No piano! That was not an insurmountable difficulty. Within a few days Helena and Wanda Janowski had a piano.

Mr. Paderewski's "fan" mail was very heavy. One day, a letter written in a round, schoolboyish hand stood out from all the others. The musician opened it himself, and read it carefully. It was signed, "Howard Grossman," and Howard said, all in one sentence, that he was eleven years old and that his mother did not know he was writing the letter.

Howard and his mother had come to Minneapolis from Montana. They both wanted to hear Mr. Paderewski play, but when they learned that the only seats left were five dollars apiece, his mother had said that they could not afford them. So Howard had decided to write to Mr. Paderewski for a signed photograph. He took music lessons, he said, and he meant to put the photograph on the piano where he could look at it as he practised. Imagine Howard's mother's surprise when Mrs. Carlyle Scott, the concert manager in Minneapolis, appeared at her door with tickets for the concert!

"Mr. Paderewski wants you and Howard to be his guests," Mrs. Scott told the astonished Mrs. Grossman.

Nor was this all. When the concert was over, Howard was escorted to Mr. Paderewski's room, and treated to a feast of cookies and candy. The great musician talked to the boy, and Howard told him about his piano lessons, his school, his teacher, and his friends.

Ignacy Paderewski loved people, but his deepest affection was for children. When he was tired and discouraged, their laughter and happy faces were like an elixir to him. He never tried to explain the joy he felt in them, for it was so much a part of him that he probably never thought it needed explanation. He had loved his invalid son dearly and he may have found comfort for his loss of Alfred in the strength and promise of other children. Or it may have been a case of the old artist, loving his art and striving to find in some young persons the assurance that that art would be carried on. But whatever it was, his love for children gave Mr. Paderewski much joy, and through it he was enabled to give generously. And there was nothing he enjoyed more than giving—not time only, but money, too. In every country of the world, it has been said, there are boys and girls having special opportunities for study because of the generosity of Ignacy Paderewski, the Polish pianist.

Twenty-one

Herbert Hoover and Ignacy Paderewski

"If it had not been for Herbert Hoover, the children of Poland would surely have died of starvation after the war with Russia," Mr. Paderewski said one day in New York when he was discussing conditions in his country.

Then he described the conditions the two directors of the Hoover Fund discovered in Poland when they travelled there. The two directors were Dr. Vernon Kellogg and Colonel William R. Grove. The machinery of war had ploughed through the land, destroying crops, with the result that there was no food. Neither was there seed to plant. Devastation and misery reigned from Poznan to Lwow, from Wilno to Krakow. The two directors spent several months in the country, and during that time distributed or set up plans for the distribution of about three and one half million dollars' worth of food and clothing. As was natural, the children had first consideration, for on them was to rest the responsibility of building the country anew.

Often when Mr. Paderewski, who loved to tell anecdotes, mentioned Mr. Hoover, a faintly reminiscent smile would curve his lips and he would say, "Let me see, ah, yes, I've known Herbert Hoover a long time, almost as long as I've known America."

And then he would tell this story:

In the year 1892 Herbert Hoover was a student at the Leland Stanford University, and Ignacy Paderewski was on his first American tour. He was to give a concert in San Francisco. It was when young Mr. Hoover, then barely eighteen years old, read the press reports of the famous musician's concerts that he had what seemed to him an unusually good idea. When he consulted a fellow student about it, he agreed that the idea was excellent. With hopes soaring to the sky, the two joined forces; they became concert managers, and approached Ignacy Paderewski with the request that he be their first "presentation."

The city the two enterprising youths selected for their first venture in the concert business was San José, California. On the warm sunny March day when Mr. Hoover and his partner went to San José to make arrangements, they may have wondered if the little city would wake up enough to respond to the opportunity they were about to give its citizens. They admitted to each other that it looked very sleepy. The people not occupied in sunning themselves were busy getting ready for the Easter fiesta.

Mr. Paderewski had already given one of the several concerts he was to give in San Francisco, when he received the invitation to go to San José. He accepted it after the two managers had guaranteed him two thousand dollars. After all, two thousand dollars was not a very large sum of money, the one manager said to the other, and they set about making preparations for the big event. Announcements were put up on billboards all over the city, and young and old alike paused to read them and look at the picture of the musician. He had an interesting face, yes, very interesting, although some may have laughed a little at his long hair and goatee. The citizens of San José began buying tickets. In a few days the two concert managers thought their worries were over, for sixteen hundred dollars had rolled in.

Four hundred dollars more and the artist's guarantee would be met. Another few hundreds and the hall would be paid for. A few more hundreds and posters and tickets would be paid for. Then incidental expenses and their profit—oh, it was going to be easy. They began to talk blithely of the concert business. They would probably make it their life work.

But, alas, the money did not continue to roll in. It had gone up to sixteen hundred dollars, and no amount of effort would make it rise higher. The concert was five days away. Then it was five hours away. The two "concert managers" sought out friends, and poured out their troubles. The friends were sympathetic, but not sufficiently to lend two students a large sum of money, probably as much as eight hundred dollars. In desperation, the two took their worries to a drug store soda fountain and over ice-cream sodas "cogitated" on what was best to do. At last they agreed to tell Mr. Paderewski of their critical financial position.

He listened attentively to the tale of their get-rich-quick scheme, and if he felt like laughing he considerately refrained from doing so.

When the whole story was told, the pianist said, "Well, first, you must pay the expenses of the concert. Next comes your profit, the usual twenty percent. I'll take what is left."

With sighs of relief and gratitude, probably better expressed by smiling countenances and brows which suddenly lost their care-worn furrows than by words, the two set about doing as Mr. Paderewski had advised. They did so, with the firm conviction that the concert business, no matter how alluring, was not for them. Doubtless, they returned to their studies with more diligence than ever before. They returned with something else, too—a great admiration for the Polish pianist, Paderewski.

Because of this early association and the friendship that grew out of it, Mr. Hoover may have had a special interest in Poland when he became head of the American Relief Administration. Certainly through the years that he was President of the United States, he revealed great knowledge of Polish problems, and showed a marked willingness to help solve the perplexities of the new, free country.

Flowers of friendship, planted in the confident days of youth—these have a fragrance and enduring bloom—so a poet might describe the beginnings of the friendship between these two men, the statesman, Herbert Hoover, and the pianist and patriot, Ignacy Paderewski.

Twenty-two

Brother and Sister Together

"We have travelled a long road, and a very crowded one, haven't we, Antonina?" Ignacy Paderewski said quietly to his sister, who had come from Poland to Switzerland to live with him.

His sister gave him an affectionate smile, but when she made no comment, he resumed in a voice that had a faraway quality in it, "Yes, a long, long road and sometimes a very rough one. Think of it, from little, muddy Sudylkow to . . ."

He did not finish the exclamation, for Antonina interrupted suddenly with, "From Sudylkow in Wolyn to the whole world, that's what it's been for you, Ignacy, a world of fame. Everyone in the whole world must surely know your name."

Mr. Paderewski smiled at the old woman, sitting in the tall wing chair by the crackling fire. She was seventy-two years old, and yet as she sat there she looked no more than fifty, and her voice, actually, had a vigorous, youthful ring in it. Her eyes glowed with pride and happiness on this particular day, for, at last, after nearly forty years of separation, she was with her brother again. The autumn wind howled tempestuously and little gusts of it descended to the fire in the grate, but Madam Antonina did not notice the yellow sparks nor hear the fire's angry sputtering. Her mind was absorbed by two thoughts, the first one, that she and her brother were together again, and the other, that this blustering day was his birthday and they were spending it together.

"Seventy to-day," Mr. Paderewski murmured and stared into the fire. "Remember when I was six, Antonina?"

Of course she remembered, and there were several birthdays before the sixth one that she remembered with equal clearness, but she had no intention of letting her brother know that just now, for he was much too fond of teasing her about her sententious memory. Moreover, she did not want him to indulge in too many reminiscences, for remembering always made Ignacy sad.

"Do you always turn back the pages of your life on your birthday?" she asked lightly.

"Well, not exactly," Mr. Paderewski answered slowly, "But really, it's good to think about the past, and one's particular past, on occasions. At least once a year."

He lit a fragrant cigarette, and settled back in his chair as if prepared to lose himself in recollections. He drew a deep sigh, then another, but before he could bring forth a third, Antonina was sitting up straight in her chair, ready to give battle to any sad memories that might arise to harass her brother.

"On your name day, you are always ready to entertain friends and laugh and joke," she said, "but on your birthday it's quite a different story. Then it's sighs and recollections and sometimes even tears. Yes, tears. You've always made me cry on your birthday."

"Cry!" Ignacy Paderewski exclaimed. "But why should you? Weren't we happy when we ran barefooted through the meadows of Sudylkow? Didn't we laugh and sing and play with Siwek? Remember how he used to neigh, Antonina? Remember his long tail and how he would toss it about and it would wave like a flag in the breeze? Tell me, isn't it good to remember those simple, joyous days? Doesn't the memory warm your old heart as it does mine?"

"To be sure," Antonina answered, "but you have no need to regret those days. It is all right to remember them, but do not be sad because we are not both there now. If you had not left Sudylkow you would not be what you are to-day."

"That's where you are wrong, Madam," Mr. Paderewski answered with a deep chuckle. "Sudylkow, New York, Morges —anywhere—it would be the same. Anywhere I would be old, seventy years old, and no one would want me, at least, no one but you, Antonina. We are old together."

"Do not speak like that, Ignacy. It is wicked." Antonina's voice was very firm. "You know quite well that you are needed and you will be needed all your life."

The two were silent for quite a long time. They stared into the fire, and in its flames and embers, each seemed to be

Mr. Paderewski when he was making the film, *Moonlight Sonata*

seeing his past—the happy years, the years of pain and grief, and the years of loneliness.

"Ah, well, they are gone now," the old musician said reflectively. "The years have gone and left us here, and we can never know if we should have been happier staying all our lives in Wolyn or not. Sometimes I think I should have been. I should have worked in the fields, perhaps, and played an untuned piano at the weddings of my friends."

Antonina, whose married name was Wilkonski, adjusted the lace collar that adorned her sombre black dress, and looked at her brother speculatively. She was not sure that he was serious; he might just be teasing her. Finally, she decided that he really was suffering from regrets, so she spoke with firm confidence.

"I am certain that it would not have been better," she said. "Think of it, you, with your great gifts, going from village to village to play worn-out pianos for your friends, while at home your children, probably as many as ten, would be crying for bread. You yourself would have gone barefoot, as we did when we were children, or you would have worn heavy boots. Once a year, at Easter, you would have carried a basket of eggs to church to have them blessed, and about thirty times a year you would have got drunk at a village tavern—" Antonina's drab picture of the past that might have been was brought to an abrupt stop by an interruption from her brother.

"I would never have had champagne," he said with a soft, musical laugh, "and I must confess, Antonina, that I love to drink it. Next to buttermilk, you know."

The two drifted into silence again. The November wind

still howled like an impatient, angry animal demanding entrance to the warm sitting-room. Perhaps Ignacy Paderewski, as he listened to the tempest, was reminded of a similar night nearly sixty years before, when a pack of wolves pursued two sleighs over the snowy road that ran from Kiev to Sudylkow. Perhaps a whimsical thought flitted through his mind—that the queer unearthly sounds that burdened the night wind now were the greedy cries of the descendants of those beasts of the Ukrainian steppes. After all, Ukrainia was not too distant from Switzerland. But whatever the musician's thoughts may have been on this night, they were, without doubt, deeply tinged with sorrow.

Except for Antonina, the dear companion of his childhood, he was alone in the world, and try as he would, he could not free himself of an oppressive sense of desolation. His father— he had no need to mourn for him, for he had died full of years and in contentment. But his first wife, Tosia—life had been snatched from her, as it had been from Alfred, their son. And now Helena, his second wife, who had been good to him and to his crippled son, had died. The old musician silently bowed his head and thanked God for the love of Antonina. She understood him, trusted him, and from babyhood they had shared so many joys. The first one, he thought now, had been Siwek. How they had loved that horse!

"Do you remember the vacation we had together in Normandy in 1893?" Mr. Paderewski asked suddenly.

Antonina put down the apple she was peeling and said, "Of course I remember. Alfred was twelve that year and he was with us. So was Edward Kerntopf."

"And I finished my 'Polish Fantasia' in five weeks," Mr. Paderewski added. "Do you remember it? For piano and orchestra, you know."

Of course Antonina remembered it. There was no event of her brother's life that she did not remember. She was, in fact, as good as any work of reference that could have been prepared on the life of Ignacy Paderewski, for every incident was filed in her mind with complete details—exact place, exact year, month and day, exact type and title of composition, exact concert, and a good résumé of the critics' reports.

Now Antonina gave her brother a demonstration of her knowledge by saying, "And what's more, Ignacy, I remember the first time you played it for an audience. It was at the festival of music in Norwich, England, with Mr. Randegger conducting."

"Is that so?" Mr. Paderewski's voice suggested doubt of this piece of information, and Antonina immediately enumerated other events of his life—some before and some after—to prove to him that he really had played the "Polish Fantasia" for the first time at Norwich. Actually, her brother had had no doubt of the accuracy of her recollections; he had merely been testing her memory for the pleasure it gave him to be reminded of the faithful way she had followed his career.

They had been separated for many years, but neither separation nor the anger she had felt toward him for having married Madam Helena Gorski, a divorcee, had caused her to lose interest in him. She had watched his success grow with as much pride as if she had been his companion on all his tours. She had been grieved when sorrow had descended on him, and she had been as full of wrath as he had been of chagrin, when he had left Warszawa after resigning the premiership of the country for which he had done so much.

Now after nearly two decades of almost complete separation, they were together again, and were to stay together for the rest of Ignacy Paderewski's life. Madam Antonina Wilkonski had lived in a small Polish community during the years of her marriage and her widowhood, until she had left it to be with her brother, yet, despite her lack of experience, she was a gracious hostess. She received her brother's friends with a simple cordiality that won their hearts, and they, one and all, became her friends. She had another talent that saved her brother much perplexity, and this was for general management. No sooner had she mastered the intricacies of the household at Morges than she began to supervise the farm. Later, when they went to California, she looked after the small estate there so well that friends said Madam Wilkonski had everything running with the precision of a Swiss clock. Farm and household management never became so onerous, however, that she could not travel with her brother. Everywhere Ignacy Paderewski went, so did his devoted sister.

In another sphere, too, Antonina proved to be a reliable helpmate. When Mr. Paderewski's secretary, Sylwin Strakacz, presented problems to him—sometimes they were political; sometimes they concerned proposed concert tours—the musician invariably said, "let us consult my sister," and usually, the two, brother and sister, arrived at a decision together. It was not that Madam Wilkonski ruled her brother; it was just that they were close together in their relationship of good companions.

Antonina may have had one rival in her brother's affections, and Ignacy Paderewski may have had one rival in his sister's affections, but as the rival was Poland, their dear country, it never caused any dissension between them. Madam Wilkonski loved Poland as devotedly as her brother did, and often as the two sat chatting in front of a fire or in their sunny garden, they talked of their native land and dreamed dreams of a future that would be happy for her. No country has ever had more sincere patriots than Poland had in Ignacy and Antonina Paderewski. The former may have made mistakes in his political career, but they were never due to selfishness. He may have loved his country more than he understood the problems of the people, but always, he was honest. He wanted the very best for Poland and her citizens.

Although his life as a statesman was brief and ended unhappily, this was never held against him by the Polish people. They loved him for his music and for his eager and constant loyalty. Throughout his life, Paderewski was never known to speak ill of anyone. He might shake his head and mutter, "Stupid fellow! Stupid! Stupid!" but when the little tempest of irritation had subsided, he would always say, "When he has had more experience, he will improve. All he needs, poor fellow, is a little more knowledge."

Throughout his life, there was one race of people for whom he showed a particular love. It was the black race. He loved their music, the eager way in which a black man or woman rendered service, and the simple manner in which they showed their affection. His sister often protested that he was much more considerate of a negro than of a white person.

A self-imposed duty of his secretary and of his sister was to watch the hand Mr. Paderewski drew from his pocket when he was giving a tip. It was an established rule with him that what he took from his pocket should be given, no matter what it was—five dollars, ten dollars, twenty dollars. Another custom was to tip elevator boys, not once a day but on every occasion on which he rode on an elevator. There must be many elevator boys who can narrate stories of tips mounting so fast that they could hardly restrain shouts of delight and astonishment.

One day in a New York hotel this habit of generous tipping resulted in a minor disaster. Mr. Paderewski and Madam Wilkonski came down in the elevator on their way to Steinway Hall where the musician was going to try out some pianos. The colored boy on the elevator flashed a merry smile, as the car came to a standstill at the main floor, and Mr. Paderewski drew a crisp bill from his pocket. The boy took it, and even though he was accustomed to amazing tips from the musician, this one was too much for him. He gasped, staggered, and fell in a faint.

Madam Wilkonski cried out, and people began to gather in curious groups. "What has happened?" everyone asked everyone else, but no one knew until the elevator boy recovered.

"See," he said, and he held out his hand for every one to see. "Mr. Paderewski gave me a hundred dollar bill! A hundred dollar bill!" The boy said it over and over again like a refrain.

Twenty-three

A Conversation with a Worker

On a day that was warm and bright with the summer's sun and fragrant with the rich perfume of pine trees and flowers, Ignacy Paderewski and his friend, Henryk Opienski, sat in the garden of Riond-Bosson, and talked, sometimes of the past, through which they had been friends, and sometimes of the future, already darkened by the shadow of Adolf Hitler. They talked quietly and with the sublime calm that occasionally comes to old people who, though they are not weary of life, are a little detached from the happenings of the present. Opienski was a composer and an orchestra conductor, but in recent years he had spent much time in writing on subjects concerned with music. For awhile they had talked of his successes but under Mr. Opienski's guidance, they turned to a subject that he found at least as interesting, that of Ignacy Paderewski's phenomenal career.

"Yes, I've followed your tours pretty carefully," Mr. Opienski said. "As a matter of fact, I've made a record of them, and in case you do not know, I shall be glad to inform you of the extent of your travelling and the number of your concerts."

Mr. Paderewski laughed. "Tell me," he said, "have I gone a million miles, do you think?"

"Not quite," his friend answered. "My record shows that you have travelled four hundred thousand miles, for the purpose of giving one thousand, six hundred concerts."

"That many!" Paderewski exclaimed.

"And it is estimated that at least seven million people have heard you play," Mr. Opienski informed his listener, and the listener appeared to be surprised.

"Seven million," he repeated with a rueful smile, and stared at his long, strong fingers, still as beautiful and agile as they had been when he was in his prime.

"Seven million," he said again, and with a chuckle added, "all that work does not show for much at my bank now."

"That is your fault," his friend replied. "You could have had millions. Some people say that you have had as much as four millions. But would you keep it? No, not you. All your life you've been flinging money about as if it were of no consequence whatever."

Mr. Opienski may have sounded as if he were scolding his friend, but the look of deep affection that shone in his eyes belied the sternness of his words. However, Mr. Paderewski had no wish to talk of his whimsical use of money.

"Come, let's walk, my friend," he said. "The day is beautiful and a turn in the park will do us both good."

The two old men, both a little uncertain on their feet, walked slowly along the broad, winding path, lined on either side by spruce trees and shrubbery. The sun sent warm, dazzling beams through the foliage of the trees and the two faces, looking a little like leaves tinged by autumn frost, lost some of their parched and old appearance. Like the flowers, it seemed, the faces of the two friends, opened and smiled at the sun. As they walked, each rested his hand on the shoulder of the other. As if he had sprung up from the path, a worker suddenly approached them, walking swiftly, as if he were intent on getting somewhere in a hurry.

"Good day," Mr. Paderewski said. "Have you heard any news to-day, my man?"

The man stopped, took his cigarette from his mouth and his cap from his head. "Nothing but trouble," he said. "But perhaps, it would be better if we'd fight Hitler now and have it over with."

Mr. Paderewski shook his head sadly. He remembered another war that had started when he was in Switzerland and he had said, "This may mean freedom for Poland." What would this new war mean to Poland, he wondered.

"What is your name?" Mr. Paderewski asked the man. "From your speech I would think you might be Polish."

The man laughed. "You are right, sir. They call me André hereabout, but I am a Pole. I belong to the western part of the country."

"The western part, ah, yes, and tell me, please, why did you leave there? The land is good, is it not? You could get work, surely." As Mr. Paderewski talked, he led the man to a seat, and, protesting, the worker allowed himself to sit down with the two old gentlemen.

"Work! To be sure, there was work," André answered, "but there was not much pay. For that reason I went to France to work in coal mines. Ugh, that was dreadful. I got sick and so I came here to try to get strong in the fine clear air of Switzerland."

"And now you are better?" Mr. Opienski asked solicitously, but before André could answer, Mr. Paderewski interrupted with a question.

"What do you do, André, here in Switzerland, where the air is so good?" he asked.

André looked a little shamed, but he answered promptly, "I clean pig pens and cow stables, and sometimes on fine days I help the gardeners dig in their gardens. Just now, I'm on my way to your place to mow the lawn and pull weeds."

André made as if to rise, but the musician put a detaining hand on his arm.

"Before you go," he said, "I want you to tell me what you, a worker, think of art. Do you sometimes go on holidays to look at pictures or to hear music being played?"

What Mr. Paderewski wanted to find out, of course, was what André thought of him, a pianist, who had spent his life giving concerts. There may have been another idea in his mind, too—that from André he might discover how the working people of his native land felt toward him.

André puffed at his cigarette, but as there was no life in

it, Mr. Opienski gave him another and held a light for him. Quite evidently this was the most expensive cigarette André had ever put to his lips.

"Why speak of art to me," he said vehemently, "when I have never, for one instant in my life, escaped the misery of poverty? Yes, to be sure, I know that music is beautiful. When I was young, I sometimes danced to it, especially at the New Year, but the need for bread has always been so urgent that I have had no time to enjoy music. No time whatever."

Mr. Paderewski drew a deep sigh, and shook his head. His grasp on André's arm tightened. In this way he conveyed his sympathy to him.

"You see, Mr. Paderewski," André said, taking courage, "we poor people have not much chance to hear you play. Once in Poland, I heard men like myself say, 'Ah, Mr. Paderewski— he does not play his music for such boors as we are."

"That is not true," Mr. Paderewski answered quickly. "I have played many times for workers. In many countries of the world, I have played for workers."

"Then few people remember it," André said, determined to say what was on his mind, now that he had an opportunity. "What I have heard in Poland, I have heard in France and here in Switzerland: Mr. Paderewski plays for the aristocrats and rich people. Always the same in every country of Europe, for I have met workers from Germany and Roumania and Czecho-Solvakia. In America it may be different. There, I do not know; it may be that workers are rich men in the United States."

"Tell me this, André," Mr. Opienski asked, "how do you

think a musician would live if he did not play for rich people? They can pay him, remember."

"You are right, sir," André said, "but the workers would have paid, too, if they had been given a chance. Oh, not so much, of course, and the critics might not have given so much attention to workers' concerts, and so the reports would not have had big headlines. Nevertheless, we workers would have paid, and the memory of the artist would have lived in our hearts and memories for all our lives."

Paderewski sat looking into the distance. He was listening to André, and yet his thoughts seemed to be far away. Perhaps in imagination, he was hearing the delighted applause of a throng of workers. Perhaps the sigh that came from his lips was heavy with regret.

André was speaking again, this time with not so much assurance. He was nervous and he stammered several times. "All your life, Mr. Paderewski, you have played in the palaces of kings and the castles of titled aristocrats and the princely mansions of rich Americans, and never in workers' club houses for the few cents we could have paid. Even though we are sorry that you overlooked us, sir, we Poles love you. Yes, love you, and are glad that by your music you have carried the name of Poland over the world."

As he was speaking, André got to his feet, and before his last words were said, he was moving away. Mr. Paderewski murmured "Good! Good!" several times, but André was not there to hear it. He had hurried away, almost at a run, probably overcome with sudden embarrassment for having spoken out so plainly and forcefully.

The sun still shone after André had gone. The birds still sang and the bees still buzzed, but the warmth of the day had gone for Mr. Paderewski. He felt cold and unhappy, so cold that he shivered and so unhappy that he wiped a tear from his eye. He knew that André had spoken the truth and he knew that now his life was too far spent for him to right the wrong he had done. The two old friends sat on the garden bench for a long time, not talking, but thinking thoughts that neither could have put into words.

"He was right, that good fellow, André," Mr. Paderewski said at last. "The world is full of workers, and yet I have spent my life going to the few rich, not because they loved music more, but because they had more dollars. Bah, what foolishness!"

Mr. Opienski tried to protest, but his friend would not allow him to do so.

"There is no need to make excuses for me, Opienski," he said. "If I had played for the poor people, they would have paid me with love and remembrance. My old heart would be warm now with their thankfulness. And think of the good I could have done! I would have made them love music and understand it. I could have played in those giant stadiums they have in all big cities. And hundreds of thousands of people could have heard me at one time. I could have filled the minds and the hearts of the world with music. Oh, Opienski, the opportunity I lost! Lost because I looked to the rich for applause. I tell you, art does not belong to the rich. It belongs to the people. To André who cleans pig pens. To his brother who works in a coal-mine. To the men and women who bend over machines in factories. To those who plant seed and tend cows. Art—music, painting, literature—it is nothing if it does not belong to the people."

Mr. Opienski understood the pain of regret that was in Mr. Paderewski's heart, for a similar one burdened him. He may have been sorry that André had spoken with such frankness, but he agreed with him, nevertheless. He knew that an artist can achieve the full greatness that is in him, only by giving his art to the people. With their appreciation to nurture it, it can grow and blossom, as a plant does.

"It is not too late," Mr. Opienski said gently. "To-day, the two of us can begin to make plans. We will work out some way to bring music to the world. Free music. No, my friend, it is not too late."

But there was no comfort for Ignacy Paderewski in this optimism. "Can you not see that I am an old man now, and helpless, so very helpless?"

Mr. Opienski shook his head.

"It is true," Mr. Paderewski said. "You remind me of an old Polish proverb: 'Are you scoffing at me, or do you really want me to show you the road?' It is too late, Opienski. Too late. Too late."

The two old men might have spent the rest of the day sitting in the garden in mournful solitude, if Mr. Paderewski's secretary had not found them at this moment.

"Here you are," he exclaimed when he saw them. "Every-one is looking for you. Guests have arrived from Paris."

Twenty-four

Rancho San Ignacio

During the closing years of his life, Ignacy Paderewski's friend, Henryk Opienski, spent a great deal of time with him. The three, Madam Wilkonski, Opienski, and Paderewski, spent many hours in front of a roaring wood fire; sometimes they sipped coffee, and frequently they entertained one another with recollections from the past of one or the other. Doubtless, Mr. Paderewski's experiences, gathered from his many tours and concerts, furnished the most laughter.

There was, for instance, the story of the important woman in Chicago, who appealed to Mr. Paderewski to get her a seat at his concert. She had been to the box office, but had met with no success. She had been to the office of the concert manager, with the same negative result.

"I suspect that the reason was not that the seats were all

sold," Mr. Paderewski said, "but that the woman was much too stout to get into a seat."

"And what did you do?" one of his listeners asked.

"I said to her, 'Madam, I have but one seat for this concert, and, naturally, I shall be happy to give it to you.'"

"And?" a listener asked, when the narrator paused to chuckle.

"'Oh thank you! Thank you!' the woman said. 'Where is it?' and I answered, 'At the piano, madam.'"

"And then what happened?" Madam Wilkonski asked.

"Nothing," her brother answered, "except that the woman refused the seat."

There was another story that the musician liked to tell. It was of a letter he received when he was in Honolulu in 1927. He might even produce the letter to let his guests read it for themselves. It read:

"Dear Mr. Payderoosky,
    Please send me one lock of hair for remembrance."

"And what did you do?" some listener was sure to ask, and the musician would recite the reply he had asked to have sent: "Dear Mr. X,

At the request of Mr. Paderewski, I am sending you one lock of hair from Mr. Paderewski's favorite horse, one lock of hair from his valet, and one from the mattress on which Mr. Paderewski sleeps. As you did not specify in your letter what kind of hair, or whose, you wanted, we are sending you all three. Please choose the one you prefer, and return the others."

Whenever Mr. Opienski heard the story of the hair being sent to Honolulu, he usually followed it with one told him by

Marcel, Mr. Paderewski's valet. He did it with a mischievous gleam in his eyes, for he suspected that his friend was none too fond of the tale.

Marcel, it seemed, had been sitting in a top balcony in Madison Square Garden for one of Mr. Paderewski's concerts.

The master came on to the stage and sat down at the piano, almost unnoticed. Quietly, as if he did not want to obtrude his music, he began playing. Gradually the vast audience of the top balcony became aware that someone with a shaggy head of long hair was at the piano. No one appeared to know who the performer was, and one near-sighted member of the audience murmured to his companion, "When is that ballerina going to stop playing the piano and begin to dance?" Mr. Opienski always repeated the answer with a gleeful chuckle: "She'll stop playing and start to dance when someone comes from behind to play for her. She's just filling in time."

The "she" was the master, Paderewski, playing music for which he had been applauded many, many times.

On this particular evening after Henryk Opienski had told the story, perhaps for the hundredth time, the two men were alone together, and Mr. Paderewski began talking of the conversation they had had months before with the worker, André.

"Remember André who expressed his thoughts so well?" Mr. Paderewski asked.

"Yes, I remember, certainly, but what brings him to your mind now?" his friend asked. "You haven't spoken of him for weeks."

"But I've been thinking about him," the other answered, "and not only of him, but of others. What he said was like an accusation against me, and really, I needed it, for during the years I have almost forgotten a dream I used to have. When I was in my thirties and forties the dream was with me constantly. Then when I got mixed up in political affairs, I deliberately put it out of my head. Now André has brought it back to me."

"Tell me," Henryk Opienski begged. "I know without you saying so, of course, that it concerns the education of people so that they can appreciate music. But what more is there?"

So Ignacy Paderewski began the narration of the dream he had dreamed many years before, and had planned to bring to reality. It had begun to take shape in his mind while he was on his first long concert tour, and through the years it had grown in details until now, as he told it to Opienski, it seemed like a practical, well-planned enterprise.

"In a short time we are going to my home in California," Mr. Paderewski said, "and after I have had a good rest, I am going to start on my free concert tour. I am determined to answer the accusation of André, you see. Then when that is over, you and I will settle down to teach music to talented children. In a few years, we should be able to start several good artists on careers that will be worthy of the names of Opienski and Paderewski."

Mr. Opienski rose from his chair and walked about the room. The proposed concert tour was no surprise to him, but the music school was. Until this moment, he had had no idea that his friend had ever thought of such a thing. Oh, yes, indeed, he had often heard him exclaim regretfully over the music talent that was going to waste in the slums of great cities like New York, London, and Paris, but that he had a plan worked out to discover and foster these gifts, was a source of considerable amazement to Mr. Opienski.

"Everything is to be free in our school," Mr. Paderewski continued. "I mean that what money I have should be spent in this way—and for tours. Free concert tours, not for me, you understand, but for the artists we shall train."

As Mr. Opienski made no comment, the pianist decided that he disapproved.

"Do you think there are not many villages in the world like my native one in Poland?" he asked a little impatiently. "Well, there are, and in many of them at this very moment, there may be a boy or a girl eating his heart out for music and for teaching, so that he may play the piano or the violin, or in fact, some kind of a horn. Poverty, it sometimes seems to me, breeds talent, and that talent needs to be rescued from the shame of poverty. It is like a flower, as I have said so often. It must be nurtured and protected. Good people have helped me all my life; then why should I not help others? Good people had confidence in me; when I was discouraged they gave me faith in myself. That is what I will do for young musicians, and they in turn will enrich the hearts and spirits of people all over the world."

As Henryk Opienski listened to his friend talk, it was easy to forget that they were two old men, drawing near the end of life's journey. He felt convinced that Ignacy Paderewski would fulfil his dream.

"It will be lovely to be the spiritual father of great talent found in the slums of the world," Mr. Paderewski murmured and sank back, exhausted, in his chair.

The Rancho San Ignacio, situated near Paso Robles in California, facing the famous Adelaide Road, had been bought and named by Ignacy Paderewski in 1913, and at the same time he had purchased an adjoining farm and called it the Rancho Santa Helena, in honor of his wife. Even before he had bought this estate, however, he had dreamed the dream which he had now unfolded for his friend, Henryk Opienski. The person who had shared it with him, and whose idea it probably was, in the first instance, was the famous actress, Helena Modrzejewska. She had bought a ranch called "Arden" near Santa Ana, California, and Paderewski had visited her there in 1905. Together, the two old friends had worked out plans for a free school for artists, but these had never materialized, for early in the year 1909 Madam Modrzejewska had died. Now, however, Paderewski returned to the old dream with all the buoyant optimism of his middle age.

"We must tell no one, remember, Henryk, until every detail is worked out," Mr. Paderewski warned. "Not even Antonina, and not my secretary. Absolutely no one."

Mr. Opienski agreed and together the two old friends sat in the sun in front of the Chalet Riond-Bosson, talking of a future that these dreams made golden. A new era for music was going to dawn in the world. The Rancho San Ignacio on the west coast of the United States was to become the safe haven of many young people who had no money to be taught music. It would be more than that: it would be a bulwark against the growing materialism that was bearing down grimly on the world.

Meanwhile, the summer of the year 1939 drifted toward autumn and daily, a shadow grew and darkened. The last roses of the summer shed their petals and the chrysanthemums came to take their place, but for all their flaming color, the long-stemmed flowers could not stay the course of the shadow spreading its gloom over the world. Paderewski walked along the flower hedges; he paused to breathe in the perfume of spruce trees; his old eyes looked far out at the haughty mountain peaks. So they had looked in the year 1914—so confident of their towering strength, so unassailable and secure. Then his eyes rested on the tall, straight trees, and he smiled at them affectionately. They were as confident of their strength as the mountain peaks were of theirs. Then he turned his mind's eye on himself. Would he let this shadow frighten him? No. Was he not as strong as the mountain peaks and the trees? He would not give up his dreams and the resolution to make them real just because the world might be engulfed in war. For the shadow was war, the war that broke with the invasion of Ignacy Paderewski's native country.

Twenty-five

Second World War

A few hours before dawn on the first day of September, 1939, a rain of deadly bombs showered down on the sleeping villages and towns and cities of Poland. Instantly, as a wounded eagle rises up to protect its nest, so the Polish people prepared to defend their homes and their country. The army moved to meet the marching foe, pouring from the west and the north. Old men and women and children, although death hurtled at them from the sky, took up the task of digging trenches and anti-tank barricades.

It was a bitter fight and an unequal one. For years the enemy, behind the cover of a pact of friendship, had been preparing for this gigantic thrust, and now like a robber he had stormed into the country while the people slept, tired from their honest labor in the fields and factories. Now his tanks, his planes, his bombs, and his guns shrieked and flung devastation over the land. On that day and through the succeeding weeks, Poland was like a mother being robbed of her children. She tried to stand, a pillar of resolution and courage, but the enemy was like a wild animal tearing her flesh and drinking her blood. Cries of agony mingled with prayers and curses. The Mother Poland trembled; her soldiers, her women, her old men, and her little children perished by the thousands. The Mother Poland tried to stand.

Ignacy Paderewski and his sister, Antonina, heard the tragic news on the very day of the attack. Indeed, almost within the hour, the radio gave out the story in the Chalet Riond-Bosson, and the two old people wept like children. Often when sorrow had come to him before, Mr. Paderewski had turned to his piano for comfort. But not now. The black and white keys offered no solace. He was helpless. His hands trembled; his shoulders were stooped; his voice was weak. Despair held him as firmly as prison chains might have done. His Mother Poland was being strangled and yet he could not lift a rifle in her defense. He could do nothing but sit crouched before his radio, listening to the tale of her devastation. He and his sister kept to themselves; their sorrow was too deep to let other eyes behold it, even though the eyes might have been filled with tears of sympathy.

The Chalet Riond-Bosson had always been a blithe place. Flowers blossomed in its gardens. Birds sang from the swaying branches of trees, and little forest animals ran in and out among its shrubbery. But now, alas, it seemed as if grim death had entered at the gate. There was no master to greet the birds, no mistress to tend the flowers. The chalet was silent, except for a few deep sobs and a few bitter laments. Poland was dying. Each day, with the news of crops destroyed, of valiant young soldiers cut down, of villages and towns bombed, and of people fleeing in search of safety they could not find, Ignacy Paderewski sank deeper and deeper into an abyss of despair. Poland dying! The Poland that he loved as a child loves its mother!

At last, at the end of September, the word came—the brutal enemy had vanquished Poland. Her life blood had soaked into her pillaged fields. Days of enslavement, that were to be as black as stormy nights, were all that lay before the country of Ignacy Paderewski.

For the time being, Poland was defeated, but not Ignacy Paderewski. When the final word of his country's defeat came to him, he, like a knight buckling on his armor, prepared to leave the quiet haven of his Swiss chalet, and go out into the world to mobilize what forces he could to come to the rescue of the land now under bondage to Nazi Germany. He went to Paris, and there assisted General Sikorski to form the government of Poland-in-exile. He himself agreed to become the head of the Polish National Council which was formed as a substitute for the Parliament that no longer could exist in Warszawa. His knowledge of America, France, and England, of all the world, in fact, proved a great asset to the new government, especially as an army was growing to act on Poland's behalf. Men who had left Poland years before to work in the coal mines of France or in the factories or on the farms of the United States and Canada suddenly became aware of their Polish origin, and announced their eagerness to take up arms for their old mother land. Some of those who went to France to offer their services had been so long away from Poland that they had forgotten how to speak the language. Yet they went—from North America, South America, Asia. And their spiritual leader, as they rallied to the standard of Poland, was the untiring patriot, Ignacy Paderewski.

Meanwhile, the war was spreading over Europe. With the tenacity of a forest fire, it swept into Norway, into Holland and Belgium, and then to France. Some men, younger by decades than Mr. Paderewski, wept and wrung their hands in despair. But not he; his face lost some of its old, parched appearance and took on a healthy, rosy glow. His footsteps became firmer and his voice lost the feeble tone of old age and weariness. It was as if a tremendous fire were burning in his body, and in very truth, it was—the fire of resolution. He was determined to expend all his strength in this battle against brute force, and as he worked tirelessly the conviction grew that justice would be victorious.

With the invasion of France, the government of Poland-in-exile was transferred to London, but before that happened Mr. Paderewski had made a much longer voyage; by way of Spain and Portugal he came to New York, for the express purpose of once more enlisting the assistance of the United States. His head was full of ideas and his heart was full of courage. Old age could not deter him. He was ready for action. Soon he was working with the committee already in existence, and almost as soon as he set foot in America he, with his sister's assistance, organized several more, some to help Polish prisoners of war, and others to bring orphaned Polish children to America and place them in Polish-American homes. Wherever people assembled to discuss the ways and means of assisting Polish people, there usually, was Ignacy Paderewski, standing straight now as a youth of twenty, and close behind him was a stooped little old woman, his sister, Madam Wilkonski. They gave their strength and their money; their only thoughts, it seemed, were to relieve the abject misery of their vanquished countrymen.

From early morning until evening, Mr. Paderewski worked, and due chiefly to his capable secretaries, his work was well organized, so that his efforts should not be wasted. He began his day when he was in the Hotel Buckingham in New York City, with a breakfast of orange juice and coffee. In the mornings, he read and wrote letters and carried on telephone conversations with government bureaus and welfare organizations. In the afternoons, he received delegates from various societies that wished to assist or were assisting in Polish relief work. He listened attentively, and every promise that he made, he saw carried out. There was no putting-off until to-morrow.

Nearly every morning between his letter writing and his luncheon, he had time to go to Steinway Hall, where he looked affectionately at the pianos and occasionally tried out a new instrument. His chief pleasure in Steinway Hall, however, came in conversations with his friend of many years, Mr. Theodore E. Steinway. If the day's work did not promise to be too heavy, he and Madam Wilkonski would take a walk along Fifty-Seventh Street and the two old people became familiar figures to the New Yorkers hurrying to and from luncheon.

Dinner, which invariably started with raspberry ice cream, came at eight o'clock. Usually, there was a Viennese schnitzel, too, and a glass of burgundy. After dinner, while he smoked an American cigarette, he discussed the next day's work with his secretaries, Mr. Strakacz and Mr. Kollupajlo. By ten o'clock at night, he was ready to go to bed and read. Most frequently, his last waking minutes were spent in reading a Polish classic. Then sleep—and dreams of a liberated homeland.

Sometimes as he drifted to sleep, he recalled his parting from his dear friend, Henryk Opienski, who had remained in Switzerland. Mr. Opienski had accompanied the brother and sister to the station at Morges and as he went with them through the hustling throng to their carriage, he had said very softly, "It is good-bye forever, Ignacy."

But Mr. Paderewski whose heart was scarred by many farewells would not have this one spoken in a mournful vein. "No, no," he said with cheerfulness that did not sound forced, "It is good-bye for awhile only. I must go to America to get help for Poland. In America I can work with no fear of spies. Our victory will come—a holy triumph over the devil of war and then—"

"It is good-bye forever," Mr. Opienski repeated.

"I will come back to a free Europe," Mr. Paderewski answered. "I will return to Poland."

This resolution was still on his lips when the train had puffed away from the station platform. Henryk Opienski, with tears in his eyes, had waved a farewell, and his lips had shaped the words, "good-bye, forever, Ignacy." And so the wheels seemed to grind out the two—"good-bye forever"—"I will return"—"good-bye forever"—"I will return"—"good-bye"—"return."

And so on many nights the memory of this sad parting mingled in Mr. Paderewski's dreams.

Twenty-six

The Last June

The month of June, 1941, was drawing to a close, and as the warm days slipped past, there was at least one old man in the City of New York who would have held them back if he could have done so, for to him these days were very precious. He would have held them to his heart and caressed them as one does a treasure, these balmy days, fragrant with the perfume of roses and livened by the twitter of birds, for as they went, something was ebbing away from him. And something was approaching—a little closer—a little closer. He knew without shadow of doubt, what was happening. Life was going away from him and death was coming. The old man was Ignacy Paderewski.

A few weeks before, he and his sister had returned from

Florida where they had gone, following the winter spent in California. They had returned because Mr. Paderewski could not be content so far away from New York. The headquarters of many of the organizations which he sponsored were in New York City. There, too, he could receive a constant stream of news about Europe. Besides, people were arriving by ship and by clipper from Europe, and some of those people were his friends and some who came bore messages from friends left behind. In New York he felt closer to the turmoil of the world; at the Rancho San Ignacio, he felt isolated and useless. So they had come back, and taken up living at the Hotel Buckingham again.

On this late June day, Mr. Paderewski lay on his bed and stared up at the ceiling. His face was deeply lined now and whenever he glanced at his sister, his eyes were full of grief. He was so tired, so very tired. Madam Wilkonski sat beside him, hour after hour. There was no need for her to break the silence by asking of what he was thinking. She knew that he was thinking of his childhood, spent in Sudylkow, and that sometimes his thoughts turned to imagining what might be happening in Sudylkow now. It was when the awareness of the present came to him that the old man tried to rouse himself to do some work. Read a letter. Dictate a reply. Make a calculation. But there was no use trying; weariness was like a millstone on him.

"Have someone telephone to Stojowski, please Antonina," he said suddenly, and then added, "I want a copy of Sienkiewicz's *Krzyzacy*."

This request for the book did not surprise Madam Wilkonski,

Madam Wilkonski in her brother's sitting-room after his death

for Henryk Sienkiewicz was a favorite author and he had
been a close friend of Mr. Paderewski. Nor did the choice
of book surprise her. *Krzyzacy* was the book that he loved best.
Many people think *Quo Vadis* the outstanding book of Sienkiewicz, but Paderewski always found more pleasure in reading
the stirring, vigorous prose of *Krzyzacy*. There was another
reason, perhaps, for him turning to this particular novel of his
old friend; in it the story of Poland's valiant stand of centuries
before against the Germanic tribes is dramatically recorded.

But why did he want to see Mr. Stojowski? He had spent
an hour with him the day before. Perhaps it was only a whim
growing out of boredom, and she decided to delay the telephone
call to this old friend. A secretary came and read from
Krzyzacy. The day was submerged by twilight and the twilight
very slowly drifted into blue night. The secretary stopped
reading and went away.

"Do you remember what Sienkiewicz said before he died?"
Mr. Paderewski murmured the question to his sister.

"Yes," she said briefly. She did not want to talk about
Sienkiewicz's death. She knew without any reference to it
what her brother was trying to tell her.

"Then say the words to me," Mr. Paderewski begged.

But Madam Wilkonski could not. She could not trust her
voice to speak steadily.

"Then I shall say them," Mr. Paderewski said, and in a firm
voice, he repeated these words, " 'I am dying too soon . . .
How sad, for I shall not see a free Poland.' "

In a few minutes he spoke again. "How strange that he
should have died before the end of the First World War, and

I shall die before the end of the Second World War. Like him, I shall not see our country liberated," he murmured.

Madam Wilkonski tried to protest, but her brother did not hear her. He had returned to his dreams. Once or twice he smiled, and once he spoke the name of Siwek. Then he seemed to go to sleep. But no, not to sleep, for almost in an instant, he was wide awake and putting out his hand for the book by Sienkiewicz. She gave it to him, and while he searched the pages for a particular passage, she left him for a few moments. As she went, he called out the suggestion that she go out for a breath of air.

Once she was gone, he resolved to do what he had been longing to do all day. He called Charles, a hotel servant, and asked him to help him to the piano. When Charles seemed dubious about allowing him to move, Mr. Paderewski said, "Then you play, Charles. Play the Polish National Anthem for me. As you play, I shall sing."

But Charles could not play, he explained. Had he not spent his childhood in Vienna, Mr. Paderewski asked. Yes, Charles admitted, but even so, he had not learned to play the piano.

"Then I will play it," Mr. Paderewski said, and before Charles could assist him, he was on his feet and moving toward the piano, which his friend, Mr. Steinway, had given him. He sat down before it and played. He played his country's national song with a mighty force. The music flowed through the apartment and out into the corridors. The night wind caught it, and bore away its thunderous notes to the street below. It rose, it flowed, it ebbed away, and must have carried a message of courage to many Polish patriots. When the song was done, he let Charles carry him back to his bed, and he lay there, smiling happily. He would die with the National Anthem of his country ringing in his ears. And in a short time, at eleven o'clock of the night of June the twenty-ninth, in the year 1941, Ignacy Jan Paderewski died. He died with the music of Poland in his ears, and in his heart there was confidence that a beautiful to-morrow would dawn for all the freedom-loving peoples of the world.

How to Pronounce Some of the Polish Proper Names Used in This Book

In preparing this book the editor decided not to use the feminine ending for the names of the women. Hence Madam Paderewski is not spelled Paderewska, but Paderewski; Wilkonski is not spelled Wilkonska; Gorski is not spelled Gorska, as is usual in Polish. The one notable exception to this is the name of the celebrated Polish actress; her name is spelled Modrzejewska. In the English-speaking world her name was spelled Modjeska.

Adamowski	Ada-mov-skee
Babianski	Bab-ian-skee
Biernacki	Beer-nat-skee
Chodkiewicz	Hod-kev-ich
Cielewicz	Chee-lev-ich
Cudnow	Tsud-nov
Gdansk	Gud-ainsk
Ignacy	Ig-nat-cee
Iwanowski	Eevan-ov-skee
Janowski	Yan-ov-skee
Kasprowicz	Kasp-rov-ich
Kierylo	Keer-i-lo
Kollupajlo	Kol-oop-ilo
Krakow	Krak-oov
Krakowski	Krak-ov-skee
Kraszewski	Krash-ev-skee
Krzyzacy	K-she-za-tsi
Kurylowka	Koor-il-ovka
Kosciuszko	Kosh-chu-shko
Lomnica	Lom-nee-tsa
Lowicki	Lov-eest-kee
Lwow	Lvoov
Mickiewicz	Mits-kav-ich
Modrzejewska	Modj-ev-ska
Noskowski	Nos-kov-skee
Nowosiolki	Novo-shul-kee
Opienski	Op-een-skee

Ostrog	Ostraug
Paderewski	Pad-er-ev-skee
Piotr	Pioter
Podole	Podola
Roguski	Rogoo-skee
Runowski	Run-ov-skee
Sejm	Same
Sienkiewicz	Shin-kiev-ich
Sikorski	Seek-or-skee
Sliwinski	Shli-vin-skee
Slowacki	Slov-at-skee
Sowinski	Sov-in-skee
Stojowski	Stoy-ov-skee
Strakacz	Stra-kach
Studzinski	Stoo-jin-skee
Sudylkow	Sud-il-kov
Szymanski	Shee-man-skee
Tosia	Toshia
Tyszkiewicz	Tish-kav-ich
Warszawa	Var-shava
Wiejska	Vee-y-ska
Wilkonski	Veelk-on-skee
Wieniawski	Veen-iav-skee
Wilno	Veel-no
Wiwulski	Vee-vol-skee
Wolyn	Volin
Zelenski	Jel-en-skee

The Compositions of Ignacy Jan Paderewski

Without Opus No.: Impromptu
Opus 1. No. 1: Prelude a Capriccio for Piano
No. 2: Minuetto for Piano (G min.)
Opus 2. Three pieces for piano:
   (1) Gavotte (E min.)
   (2) Melodie (C maj.)
   (3) Valse Melancolique (A maj.)
   (Unnumbered) Intermezzi (G min. and C maj.)
Opus 3. Krakowiak for Piano
Opus 4. Elegy for Piano
Opus 5. Polish Dances (Tance Polskie) for Piano; also for piano four-hand
   arrangements
   (1) Krakowiak (E maj.)
   (2) Mazurek (E min.)
   (3) Krakowiak (B flat maj.)
Opus 6. Introduction and Toccata for Piano
   (Unnumbered) Moment Musical
Opus 7. Four Songs. Poems by Asnyk: Texts in Polish, German, English
   (1) The Day of Roses: Gdy ostatnia roza zwiedla
   (2) To My Faithful Steed: Siwy Koniu
   (3) The Birch Tree and the Maiden: Szumi w gaju brzezina
   (4) My Love is Sent Away: Chlopca mego mi zabrali
Opus 8. Chants du Voyageur: Five Pieces for Piano
   (1) Allegro agitato
   (2) Andantino
   (3) Andantino grazioso: (Melody in B maj.) arranged for violin or
   cello and piano; also for orchestra
   (4) Andantino mistico
   (5) Allegro giocoso
Opus 9. Polish Dances:
   Folio I: (1) Krakowiak (F maj.)
          (2) Mazurek (A min.)
          (3) Mazurek (A maj.)
   Folio II: (4) Mazurek (B flat)
          (5) Krakowiak (A maj.)
          (6) Polanaise (B maj.)

Opus 10. Maytime Album, Album de Mai, Scenes Romantiques for Piano
    (1) In the Evening: Au Soir
    (2) Love Song: Chant d'amour
    (3) Scherzino
    (4) Barcarolle
    (5) Caprice Valse
Opus 11. Variations and Fugue on an Original Theme. A Minor, for Piano
Opus 12. Tatra Album (Dances of Zakopane Mountaineers)
    Originally for Piano, four hands. For two hands.
Opus 13. Sonata for Violin and Piano (A min.)
Opus 14. Humoresques de Concert for Piano
  Book I (a l'antique)
    (1) Menuet in G
    (2) Sarabande
    (3) Caprice (genre Scarlatti)
  Book II (moderne)
    (4) Burlesque
    (5) Intermezzo Polacco
    (6) Cracovienne Fantastique
Opus 15. In the Desert. Dans le desert—Musical Tableau
Opus 16. Miscellanea: Series of Piano Pieces
    (1) Legende No. 1 (A flat maj.)
    (2) Melodie (G flat maj.)
    (3) Theme varie (A maj.)
    (4) Nocturne (B flat maj.)
    (5) Legende No. 2 (A maj.)
    (6) Moment Musical
    (7) Menuet (A maj.)
Opus 17. Concerto in A Minor for Piano and Orchestra
Opus 18. Six Songs to poems by Mickiewicz, with Piano Accompaniment
    (Polish, English and German texts)
    (1) Mine Eyes Have Known Tears: Polaly sie lzy
    (2) The Piper's Song: Piosnka Dudziarza
    (3) My Own Sweet Maiden: Moja pieszczotka
    (4) By Mighty Waters: Nad woda wielka
    (5) Pain Have I Endured: Tylem wytrwal
    (6) Might I But Change Me: Gdybym sie zmienil
Opus 19. Polish Fantasy on Original Themes for Piano and Orchestra
Opus 20. Sonata (E flat min.) for Piano
Opus 21. Twelve Songs to Poems by Catulle Mendes
    (1) In the Forest: Dans la foret
    (2) Your Heart Is Pure Gold: Ton cœur est d'or pur
    (3) The Skies Are Very Low: Le Ciel est tres bas

    (4) Not Long Ago: Naguere
    (5) A Young Shepherd: Le Jeune Patre
    (6) She Walks with Faltering Step: Elle marche d'un pas distrait
    (7) The Nun: La Jeune nonne
    (8) Vacuity: Viduite
    (9) The Cold Moon: Lune froide
   (10) Quarrelsome: Querelleuse
   (11) The Fatal Love: L'Amour fatal
   (12) The Enemy: L'Ennemie

Opus 23. Variations and Fugue for Piano (E flat min.)
    (Unnumbered) Canzone (Song Without Words) for Piano.
    (Unnumbered) Manru. Opera in Three Acts: Orchestral score; piano score with words: libretto in Polish and German

Opus 24. Symphony (B min.) (Full score, orchestral parts and miniature orchestral score)
    (Unpublished) Cantata for Chorus and Orchestra to a poem of Tetmajer
    Violin Concerto (unfinished)
    Series of Etudes for Piano

Index

This is, for the most part, a place and person index, not a subject index, although a few subjects are included. In one instance, at least, it is not consistent; this is in the listings of Madam Antonina Paderewski-Wilkonski. The reader will observe that these are placed under "p," not "w." There are no listings under the name of the subject of the book, Ignacy Jan Paderewski.

Index

Index

Index

Index

7665

DATE DUE

DATE DUE			
SEP 02 '77 *pd*			
9/13/77			
SEP 13 '77			
OCT 12 '77			
SEP 26 '77			
SEP 26 1984			
SEP 18 1984			
SEP 18 1984			
GAYLORD			PRINTED IN U.S.A.